STRATEGIES

TO

ACHIEVE

READING

SUCCESS

STARS™ Series
Book
3

CURRICULUM
ASSOCIATES®, Inc.

ISBN 0-7609-0695-5
©2000—Curriculum Associates, Inc.
North Billerica, MA 01862

TABLE OF CONTENTS

TABLE OF CONTENTS

PART ONE: LEARN ABOUT MAIN IDEA

Read what Louis wrote about frogs. As you read, think about the most important idea in the paragraph.

Frogs change as they grow. They begin as eggs. A frog egg looks like a tiny black dot in jelly. In time, a frog egg changes into a tadpole. A tadpole has a tail. It breathes underwater and has gills like a fish. Later, the tadpole develops legs, and its tail gets shorter. It grows lungs to replace its gills. The tadpole is now a frog that can live on land!

egg → **tadpole** → **frog**

The most important idea in Louis's paragraph is **Frogs change as they grow**.

The most important idea in a paragraph is called the **main idea**. The main idea tells what a paragraph is mostly or mainly about.

★ The main idea is sometimes found in the first sentence of a paragraph.

★ The main idea is sometimes found in the last sentence of a paragraph.

★ The main idea is sometimes not found in the paragraph. You can figure out the main idea by thinking about the most important idea in the paragraph.

Read this paragraph about Ben. As you read, think about the main idea
of the paragraph. Then answer the questions.

Sick Day

Ben picked up a book and started to read. After a few minutes,
he closed the book with a sigh. Then he turned on the television.
Ben flipped through a dozen channels, but he couldn't find
anything to look at. His lunch sat on the table by his bed.
He wasn't even hungry. Ben had to admit that staying home sick
was boring.

1. What is the main idea of the
   paragraph?
   Ⓐ Ben doesn't feel like eating.
   Ⓑ Ben likes to read when he is sick.
   ⬤ Staying home sick can be boring.
   Ⓓ There is nothing on television
   during the day.

2. Where or how did you find the
   main idea?
   Ⓐ in the first sentence of the
   paragraph
   ⬤ in the last sentence of the
   paragraph
   Ⓒ in the middle of the paragraph
   ⬤ by thinking about the most
   important idea in the paragraph

Work with a partner. Talk about your answers to questions 1 and 2.
Tell why you chose the answers you did.

Remember: The main idea tells what a paragraph is mostly or mainly about.

★ Read the first sentence of the paragraph. The main idea is sometimes found here.

★ Read the last sentence of the paragraph. The main idea is sometimes found here.

★ Sometimes, the main idea is not found in a sentence from the paragraph. You can figure out the main idea by thinking about the most important idea in the paragraph.

Read this article about new-year celebrations. As you read, ask yourself, "What is the article mostly about?" Then answer the questions.

When do you celebrate the new year? In the United States, Europe, and Japan, most people celebrate the new year on January 1. In China, the new year begins sometime between the middle of February and the middle of March. Jewish people celebrate the Jewish new year in the fall. In Iran, the new year begins on the first day of spring.

3. What is the article mostly about?
   Ⓐ Most countries celebrate the new year on January 1.
   Ⓑ The new year begins on a different day each year.
   Ⓒ People celebrate the new year at different times.
   Ⓓ Jewish people begin the new year in the fall.

4. Where or how did you find the main idea?
   Ⓐ in the first sentence of the paragraph
   Ⓑ in the last sentence of the paragraph
   Ⓒ in the middle of the paragraph
   Ⓓ by thinking about the most important idea in the paragraph

Look at the answer choices for each question. Read why each answer choice is correct or not correct.

3. What is the article mostly about?

   Ⓐ Most countries celebrate the new year on January 1.

   This answer is not correct because the article tells you that many countries celebrate the new year on different days.

   Ⓑ The new year begins on a different day each year.

   This answer is not correct because the new year is not on a different day each year. Different people celebrate the new year on different days.

   ● People celebrate the new year at different times.

   This answer is correct because it tells about all the ideas in the article. It is the most important idea. It tells what the article is mostly about.

   Ⓓ Jewish people begin the new year in the fall.

   This answer is not correct because it is not the most important idea of the article. It does not tell what the article is mostly about.

4. Where or how did you find the main idea?

   Ⓐ in the first sentence of the paragraph

   This answer is not correct because the first sentence is "When do you celebrate the new year?" This is not the most important idea in the article.

   Ⓑ in the last sentence of the paragraph

   This answer is not correct because the last sentence is "In Iran, the new year begins on the first day of spring." This is not the most important idea in the article.

   Ⓒ in the middle of the paragraph

   This answer is not correct because the middle of the paragraph tells about when people in China celebrate the new year. Also, the main idea is more often found in the first or last sentence of a paragraph, not the middle.

   ● by thinking about the most important idea in the paragraph

   This answer is correct because the main idea is not found in the first sentence, the last sentence, or the middle of the paragraph. The main idea is found by thinking about the most important idea in the article. This answer tells about all the other ideas in the article.

★ Each paragraph in a reading passage has one main idea. A whole reading passage, with two or more paragraphs, also has one main idea. The main idea of a whole reading passage is often found in the first or last paragraph.

★ The title of a reading passage tells something about the main idea.

Read this article about birds. Then answer the questions.

Outside and Inside

Birds have two kinds of feathers. The outside feathers help keep the bird dry. These feathers cover each other. They form a kind of raincoat for the bird. These outside feathers are flat and smooth.

Under these outside feathers is a different kind of feather. These feathers are called "down." Down feathers are soft and fluffy. Down feathers are right next to the bird's skin. The down keeps the bird warm. Baby birds have only down feathers. As they get bigger, the outer feathers grow in.

5. What is the main idea of the first paragraph?
   Ⓐ Outside feathers are flat and smooth.
   Ⓑ Outside feathers keep birds dry.
   Ⓒ Feathers keep a bird dry.
   Ⓓ All birds have feathers.

6. What is the main idea of the last paragraph?
   Ⓐ Down feathers keep birds warm.
   Ⓑ Down feathers are fluffy.
   Ⓒ Feathers keep birds warm.
   Ⓓ Baby birds have only down feathers.

7. What is the article mostly about?
   Ⓐ As birds get bigger, their outer feathers grow in.
   Ⓑ Birds have two kinds of feathers.
   Ⓒ All birds have feathers.
   Ⓓ Feathers are called "down."

8. What is another good title for this article?
   Ⓐ "Baby Birds"
   Ⓑ "Where to Find Birds"
   Ⓒ "How Birds Fly"
   Ⓓ "All About Feathers"

Read this story about Tim. Then answer the questions.

Tim rushed into the house and called for his mother. He couldn't wait to tell her about his first day at camp.

"Camp was great," said Tim. "I met a lot of kids, and we had fun together swimming, playing basketball, and painting." Mother smiled. She was glad Tim had had a good day. Tim had not been excited about going to a new camp.

"I met one girl who's from California. She's here visiting her grandmother. Her mother is a doctor. She's an only child, so she gets lonely sometimes. She's going into third grade, like me. We have lots in common, too. She likes tennis and lizards and collects stamps."

"And what's this girl's name?" asked Mother.

"How would I know?" said Tim, surprised by his mother's question. "Kids don't talk about personal stuff, Mom." Mother chuckled as Tim went outside to play with his neighborhood friends.

9. What is the main idea of paragraph two?
   (A) Tim did not want to go to camp.
   (B) Tim had fun swimming at camp.
   (C) Tim had had a good day at camp.
   (D) Tim looked for his mother.

10. What is the main idea of paragraph three?
   (A) Tim met a new friend.
   (B) Tim had fun swimming.
   (C) Mother was happy that Tim had enjoyed his day.
   (D) Tim had trouble making new friends.

11. The story is mostly about
   (A) how to make new friends.
   (B) playing sports.
   (C) a first day at camp.
   (D) things people do at camp.

12. What is a good title for this story?
   (A) "Trouble at Camp"
   (B) "Girl from California"
   (C) "Fun at Camp"
   (D) "Tim's New Friend"

★ A test question about the main idea may ask you what a reading passage is *mostly* or *mainly* about.

★ A test question about the main idea may ask you to choose the best title for a reading passage. A good title tells something about the main idea of the whole reading passage.

Here is an article about a famous house. Read the article. Then do Numbers 13 and 14.

The White House is the most famous home in the United States. This is where the President and his family live.

The President's home was not always called the White House. At different times, it was called the President's Mansion, the President's Palace, and the President's House.

The President's House was burned by the British in 1812. Workers painted it bright white to cover the black walls. Soon, people began to call it the White House. The name stuck. In time, the name was officially changed to the White House.

Finding Main Idea

13. The article is mostly about
    Ⓐ where the president lives.
    Ⓑ how the White House got its name.
    Ⓒ when the White House was burned.
    Ⓓ who painted the White House.

Finding Main Idea

14. Which of these is the best title for the article?
    Ⓐ "Famous Homes"
    Ⓑ "The President's Mansion"
    Ⓒ "One Famous House, Many Names"
    Ⓓ "Mansions and Palaces"

Here is a fable about an ant and a grasshopper. Read the fable.
Then do Numbers 15 and 16.

The Ant and the Grasshopper

In a field one summer day, Grasshopper was hopping about, chirping and singing to his heart's content. Ant passed by, carrying a kernel of corn he was taking to his nest.

"Why do you work so hard?" asked Grasshopper. "Come and chat with me."

"I am storing food for the winter," said Ant. "You should do the same."

"Why bother about winter?" said Grasshopper. "We have plenty of food right now." But Ant went on his way and continued his work.

Grasshopper continued being lazy, and, when the winter came, he had no food. He saw the ants sharing corn and grain every day from the food they had collected in the summer. Then Grasshopper knew: *Prepare today for the things you need tomorrow!*

Finding Main Idea

15. The fable is mostly about
    Ⓐ busy ants.
    Ⓑ a hungry grasshopper.
    Ⓒ planning for the winter.
    Ⓓ sharing with others.

Finding Main Idea

16. Another good title for the fable is
    Ⓐ "Plan for Tomorrow."
    Ⓑ "Take Time to Chirp and Sing."
    Ⓒ "Hard Work Can Be Fun."
    Ⓓ "Helpful Neighbors."

PART ONE: LEARN ABOUT FACTS AND DETAILS

Read this paragraph about animals. The main idea is found in the first sentence. It is underlined for you. As you read, think about the sentences that tell more about the main idea.

<u>Many different kinds of animals live on mountains</u>. Snow leopards and yaks live in the Himalayas of Asia. Mountain people herd llamas and alpacas in the Andes of South America. Mountain lions and grizzly bears roam in the North American Rockies.

The sentences that tell more about the main idea are
Snow leopards and yaks live in the Himalayas of Asia.
Mountain people herd llamas and alpacas in the Andes of South America.
Mountain lions and grizzly bears roam in the North American Rockies.

Sentences that tell more about the main idea are called **facts and details**. Facts and details help explain the main idea.

★ Facts and details tell more about the main idea.

★ Facts and details often tell about the *who, what,* and *why* of the main idea.

Read this story about Tia. The main idea is found in the last sentence. It is underlined for you. As you read, think about the facts and details that tell more about the main idea. Then answer the questions.

> Tia lives in California. Her mother is going out of town. Tia will visit her cousin Tomás in New York while her mother is away. Tia has never been to New York. She has never even been on an airplane. <u>Tia is excited about her taking her first plane ride</u>.

1. Who lives in New York?
   - Ⓐ Tia
   - Ⓑ Tia's grandfather
   - Ⓒ Tia's cousin
   - Ⓓ Tia's mother

2. Which detail tells why Tia is going to New York?
   - Ⓐ She has never been on an airplane.
   - Ⓑ Her mother is going out of town.
   - Ⓒ She wants to meet her cousin.
   - Ⓓ She is joining her mother on a trip.

 Work with a partner. Talk about your answers to questions 1 and 2. Tell why you chose the answers you did.

Remember: Facts and details explain the main idea.

★ Look for sentences that tell more about the main idea.

★ Look for sentences that tell about the *who*, *what*, and *why* of the main idea.

Read this part of the story that tells more about Tia. As you read, ask yourself, "What is the main idea? What information tells *more* about the main idea?" Then answer the questions.

Tia is packing for her trip. She is leaving for New York in four hours. So far, Tia has packed her stuffed animals, her favorite books, and her new toys. Tia has also packed her rock collection and dolls. Her suitcase is almost full.

"All of your clothes are still on your bed," says Tia's mother. "There's no room in your suitcase for them."

"That's okay," says Tia. "I have the things I *really* need."

3. When is Tia leaving for New York?
   Ⓐ in four days
   Ⓑ in one week
   Ⓒ in the morning
   Ⓓ in four hours

4. Which detail tells about something Tia is packing for her trip?
   Ⓐ Her suitcase is almost full.
   Ⓑ Tia is packing for her trip.
   Ⓒ Tia has also packed her rock collection and dolls.
   Ⓓ "All of your clothes are still in your closet," says Tia's mother.

Look at the answer choices for each question. Read why each answer choice is correct or not correct.

3. When is Tia leaving for New York?

   Ⓐ in four days

   This answer is not correct because the second sentence states that Tia is leaving in four hours, not four days.

   Ⓑ in one week

   This answer is not correct because the second sentence states that Tia is leaving in four hours.

   Ⓒ in the morning

   This answer is not correct because there is nothing in this part of the story that tells about something happening in the morning.

   ● in four hours

   This answer is correct because the second sentence is "She is leaving for New York in four hours."

4. Which detail tells about something Tia is packing for her trip?

   Ⓐ Her suitcase is almost full.

   This answer is not correct because it does not tell about something that Tia is packing in her suitcase.

   Ⓑ Tia is packing for her trip.

   This answer is not correct because it tells that Tia is packing, but it does not tell about what she is packing.

   ● Tia has also packed her rock collection and dolls.

   This answer is correct because it tells about two things that Tia has packed in her suitcase for her trip.

   Ⓓ "All of your clothes are still in your closet," says Tia's mother.

   This answer is not correct because it tells about something that is not in Tia's suitcase.

Writers use facts and details for many reasons.
When you read, look for sentences that

★ describe a person, place, or thing.

★ tell the order in which things happen.

★ explain how to do something.

Read this article about metals. Then answer the questions.

Metals

There are many different kinds of metals. Most metals are bright and shiny. One metal, iron, is used to make steel. Steel is important because it is needed to build cars, buildings, and bridges.

Gold and silver are also metals. They have been used to make jewelry and coins for thousands of years.

Most metals change when they are heated. When they are heated, they can be stretched or pressed. Wire is made by stretching and pulling metal. Aluminum foil is made by pressing metal into a thin sheet. Gold can also be made into a foil. But don't wrap your sandwich in it! Gold foil is expensive.

5. Steel is important because it is used to make
   Ⓐ jewelry.
   Ⓑ wire.
   Ⓒ bridges.
   Ⓓ gold foil.

6. Which of these tells more about the main idea of the last paragraph?
   Ⓐ Gold and silver are also metals.
   Ⓑ When they are heated, metals can be stretched or pressed.
   Ⓒ Iron is used to make steel.
   Ⓓ There are many different kinds of metals.

7. Most metals are
   Ⓐ bright and shiny.
   Ⓑ rough and dull.
   Ⓒ long and thin.
   Ⓓ hard and thick.

8. How is aluminum foil made?
   Ⓐ by stretching metal
   Ⓑ by pressing metal
   Ⓒ by pulling metal
   Ⓓ by tearing metal

Read this journal entry written by Mae. Then answer the questions.

Saturday, May 5

Today, Hal and I went to the school fair. There were lots of rides and games. There was also lots of food—hot dogs, popcorn, and fried dough. Hal and I had fun. He spent all of his money on food. I spent most of my money on games.

My favorite game was dunk the teacher. Ms. Ortiz, my favorite teacher, sat in a booth. Below her was a tank of water. I had three chances to hit a target. Any ball that hit the target would send Ms. Ortiz into the water. I couldn't help smiling as I threw each ball. Each ball I threw hit the target! I hope that Ms. Ortiz still likes me on Monday!

9. Which detail tells about Hal?
   Ⓐ There were lots of rides and games.
   Ⓑ I hope Ms. Ortiz still likes me on Monday!
   Ⓒ I spent most of my money on games.
   Ⓓ He spent all of his money on food.

10. What is a detail that tells about the main idea of paragraph two?
   Ⓐ Each ball I threw hit the target!
   Ⓑ There was also lots of food—hot dogs, popcorn, and fried dough.
   Ⓒ I spent most of my money on games.
   Ⓓ Today, Hal and I went to the school fair.

11. Ms. Ortiz is
   Ⓐ Hal's teacher.
   Ⓑ the school principal.
   Ⓒ Mae's favorite teacher.
   Ⓓ Mae's neighbor.

12. Which of these is a fact from the journal entry?
   Ⓐ Mae spent most of her money on games.
   Ⓑ Mae missed her target three times.
   Ⓒ Hal is Mae's brother.
   Ⓓ Hal's favorite game was dunk the teacher.

★ A test question about facts and details may ask you about something that happened in a reading passage.

★ A test question about facts and details may ask you about the *who, what,* and *why* of the main idea.

Here is a story about Hector. Read the story.
Then do Numbers 13 and 14.

"I'm going outside to play," Hector called to his father.

"Now?" asked Father. "Don't you want to wait?"

"Wait for what?" Hector asked as he ran out the door. Hector didn't hear his father chuckling as the door slammed shut.

When Hector got outside, he looked around. First, he looked into the neighbor's yard to see if Alex was out. The yard was empty. Then he looked up the street to see if anyone was in the park. All he saw there was a bird pecking the ground for worms.

"What happened to everyone?" Hector wondered.

Finally, Hector looked at his watch. "I guess 7:30 is a little early to go out and play," he said to himself as he walked back to his house.

Recalling Facts and Details

13. Hector told his father that he was going
   Ⓐ outside to play.
   Ⓑ to the park.
   Ⓒ to Alex's house.
   Ⓓ back to bed.

Recalling Facts and Details

14. What did Hector see in the park?
   Ⓐ a puppy
   Ⓑ a friend
   Ⓒ a bird
   Ⓓ a nest

Here is an article about the human body. Read the article.
Then do Numbers 15 and 16.

A Different Kind of Machine

The human body is like a machine that never stops working. Every minute, your heart is beating. It pumps blood through your body with each beat.

Your brain is also always busy. It sends thousands of messages to other parts of your body. These messages travel at more than 100 miles an hour! These messages tell your ears about sounds. They also tell your eyes about pictures you see. Your body is always at work, even when you sleep.

human heart

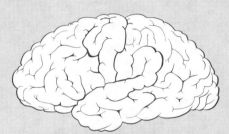

human brain

Recalling Facts and Details

15. Which detail tells more about the human heart?
    Ⓐ Your brain is always busy.
    Ⓑ It pumps blood through your body with each beat.
    Ⓒ Your body is always at work, even when you sleep!
    Ⓓ The human body is like a machine that never stops working.

Recalling Facts and Details

16. Messages from your brain travel at
    Ⓐ more than 1,000 miles an hour.
    Ⓑ less than 10 miles an hour.
    Ⓒ more than 100 miles an hour.
    Ⓓ less than 1 mile an hour.

STRATEGY 3

PART ONE: LEARN ABOUT SEQUENCE

Read the story about Aimee. As you read, think about the order in which things happen in the story.

Aimee's Big Idea

Aimee needed money to buy her father a birthday present. She had an idea. First, Aimee got out some paper cups. Next, she made a big pitcher of lemonade. Last, she made a sign that read Lemonade: 25 cents.

The order in which things happen in the story is
First, Aimee got out some paper cups.
Next, she made a big pitcher of lemonade.
Last, she made a sign that read Lemonade 25 cents.

The order in which things happen in a reading passage is called **sequence**. Sequence tells what happened first, what happened second, and so on.

★ Clue words such as *first, next, then, last, finally, before,* and *after* often tell the order in which things happen.

★ Clues such as times of day, days of the week, months, and years tell when things happen.

★ Sometimes, there are no clue words. Thinking about the beginning, the middle, and the ending of a reading passage will help you understand the order in which things happen.

Read this article about how a snake sheds its skin. As you read, think about what a snake does first, second, and so on. Then answer the questions.

How a Snake Sheds Its Skin

As a snake grows, its skin becomes too tight. When this happens, the snake grows a new skin underneath the old one. When the new skin is ready, the snake sheds its old skin.

A snake follows several steps to shed its skin. First, the snake rubs against rough objects to rip its skin. Next, it crawls against the ground or through narrow places to strip off the skin. Finally, the outside layer of scaly skin comes off. This old skin looks like an empty snake!

1. What does a snake do first to shed its skin?
   Ⓐ It crawls against the ground.
   Ⓑ It rubs against rough objects.
   Ⓒ It goes off to a quiet place.
   Ⓓ It crawls through narrow places.

2. In the article, which clue word tells what the snake does last?
   Ⓐ first
   Ⓑ last
   Ⓒ finally
   Ⓓ next

 Work with a partner. Talk about your answers to questions 1 and 2. Tell why you chose the answers you did.

Remember: Sequence tells the order in which things happen.

★ Look for clue words such as *first, next, then, last, finally, before,* and *after.*
These clue words often tell the order in which things happen.

★ Look for clues that tell about times of day, days of the week, months, and years.

★ When there are no clue words, think about the beginning, the middle,
and the ending of the reading passage. This will help you understand the
order in which things happen.

**Read this story about Kate and her brother. As you read, ask yourself,
"What happened first? What happened next?" Then answer the questions.**

Today is Saturday. Kate is baby-sitting for her little brother, Max.
Max is two years old and very active. Kate has planned
a busy day.

First, Kate is going to take Max to the
library. Next, Kate will help him find books
about dinosaurs. Max won't read any books
that don't have dinosaurs in them!

After they go to the library, Kate and Max
will walk to the ice-cream store. Then they
can eat their ice-cream cones and watch the
ducks. Last, they will walk home. Kate and
Max will cuddle up on the couch, and Kate
will read to her little brother.

3. After they go to the library,
Kate and Max will
Ⓐ go home.
Ⓑ read a book.
Ⓒ watch the ducks.
Ⓓ walk to the ice-cream store.

4. Which clue word tells what
Kate and Max will do second?
Ⓐ first
Ⓑ next
Ⓒ after
Ⓓ last

Look at the answer choices for each question. Read why each answer choice is correct or not correct.

3. After they go to the library, Kate and Max will
    Ⓐ go home.

    This answer is not correct because this is what Kate and Max will do after they get their ice-cream cones and after they watch the ducks.

    Ⓑ read a book.

    This answer is not correct because this is what Kate and Max will do after they walk home.

    Ⓒ watch the ducks.

    This answer is not correct because the third paragraph states "After they go to the library, Kate and Max will walk to the ice-cream store. Then they can eat their ice-cream cones and watch the ducks."

    ● walk to the ice-cream store.

    This answer is correct because the third paragraph states "After they go to the library, Kate and Max will walk to the ice-cream store."

4. Which clue word tells what Kate and Max will do second?
    Ⓐ first

    This answer is not correct because this clue word tells about what Kate and Max will do first.

    ● next

    This answer is correct because this clue word tells about what Kate and Max will do second. The second paragraph states "First, Kate is going to take Max to the library. Next, Kate will help him find books about dinosaurs."

    Ⓒ after

    This answer is not correct because this clue word tells about what Kate and Max will do third.

    Ⓓ last

    This answer is not correct because this clue word tells about the fifth thing that Kate and Max will do.

Many reading passages tell details and events in the order in which they happened. Look for sequence in these kinds of reading passages:

★ stories, fables, and folktales

★ articles

★ directions

★ journal entries

Read this article about a steamboat. Then answer the questions.

The Steamboat *Virginia*

Long ago, steamboats traveled up and down the big rivers of America. One of the most beautiful steamboats was the *Virginia*. The *Virginia* traveled along the Ohio River.

The weather turned rainy on one trip down the river in 1909. It rained and rained and rained. The Ohio River soon began to flood. The fields on both sides of the river filled with water.

The rushing Ohio River carried the steamboat *Virginia* over its banks. The *Virginia* floated into a flooded cornfield. The bottom of the steamboat hit the ground. The steamboat was stuck!

Then the sun came out and the water soon went down. But the lovely *Virginia* was far from the river. The steamboat sat in the middle of the cornfield.

Finally, a crew of men dug the *Virginia* out of the cornfield. They dragged the steamboat to the river. The *Virginia* was now back in its true home—the Ohio River.

5. Which of these happened first?
   Ⓐ The steamboat was stuck.
   Ⓑ The weather turned rainy.
   Ⓒ The *Virginia* floated into a flooded cornfield.
   Ⓓ The *Virginia* was back in its true home.

6. After it began to rain,
   Ⓐ the river began to flood.
   Ⓑ the water went down.
   Ⓒ the sun came out.
   Ⓓ the steamboat went faster.

7. The clue word that tells you what happened last is
   Ⓐ *then*.   Ⓒ *after*.
   Ⓑ *finally*.   Ⓓ *next*.

8. What did the men do after they dug the steamboat out of the cornfield?
   Ⓐ They took a trip down the river.
   Ⓑ They waited for the rains to come.
   Ⓒ They left the steamboat in the field.
   Ⓓ They dragged the steamboat to the river.

Read this story about a family vacation. Then answer the questions.

The Chans went on a short vacation to the shore. They planned to go to the beach for swimming, boating, and fishing.

On Friday, they wanted to go boating, but it was too windy. On Saturday, they wanted to go fishing, but it was too rainy. On Sunday, they wanted to go swimming, but it was too cold. The Chans stayed indoors for three days. Before they go away again, they will be sure to find out about the weather!

9. In the story, clues that tell about the order of events are
   (A) days of the week.
   (B) times of day.
   (C) years.
   (D) months of the year.

10. What happened on Friday?
   (A) It was rainy.
   (B) It was windy.
   (C) It was cloudy.
   (D) It was cold.

11. Which of these did the Chans want to do on Sunday?
   (A) stay indoors
   (B) go boating
   (C) go fishing
   (D) go swimming

12. Before the Chans go away again, they will
   (A) plan to stay away more than three days.
   (B) find a different place to go.
   (C) find out about the weather.
   (D) find a place where they can stay indoors.

★ A test question about sequence may ask you when certain things happened in a reading passage.

★ A test question about sequence may ask you to put events from a reading passage in order.

★ A test question about sequence may contain words such as *first, second, last, before,* or *after.*

Here is a review of a new mystery book. Read the book review. Then do Numbers 13 and 14.

Night Sounds is Mary Reed's latest mystery book for young readers. The setting is an eerie mansion near the Maine shore. Gayle and Vic Brown are staying with their uncle, who lives in the mansion. The plot is about the strange sounds that the children begin to hear. They seem to be coming from inside the walls, and are heard only at night. The children tell Uncle Evan, but he doesn't seem to be worried.

Things soon begin to disappear, and the sounds get louder. When the children talk to Uncle Evan, he begins to act strange. The children decide to solve the mystery on their own. The things they find out will send chills up your spine! And the ending is sure to surprise all readers.

If you like a good mystery story, read *Night Sounds*. But don't read it if you're alone in the house on a dark, stormy night!

Understanding Sequence

13. In the book review, which part of the book is described first?

Ⓐ the setting

Ⓑ the plot

Ⓒ the ending

Ⓓ the characters

Understanding Sequence

14. After the children first hear the sounds, they

Ⓐ see their uncle acting strange.

Ⓑ tell their uncle.

Ⓒ solve the mystery.

Ⓓ run from the mansion.

Here is an article about a well-known baseball player. Read the article. Then do Numbers 15 and 16.

Jackie Robinson was born in 1919. As a child, Jackie learned that not all people were treated the same. Because he was an African American, Jackie was not allowed to swim in public pools. He could sit only in certain places in movie theaters. Still, Jackie knew that he was as good as any other person.

Jackie joined the Brooklyn Dodgers in 1947. He became the first African American to play major-league baseball. Life was not easy for Jackie. Players on his own team called him names. Many times, he wanted to quit the team. But Jackie didn't quit. He stayed and helped his team win many games.

Jackie left baseball in 1957. He was entered into the Baseball Hall of Fame in 1962. He died in 1972. Jackie Robinson helped show that all people should be treated the same.

Understanding Sequence

15. Which of these happened first?
   Ⓐ Jackie became the first African American to play major-league baseball.
   Ⓑ Jackie was not allowed to swim in public pools.
   Ⓒ Players on his own team called him names.
   Ⓓ Jackie was entered into the Baseball Hall of Fame.

Understanding Sequence

16. The boxes tell some of the events in the life of Jackie Robinson.

Jackie left baseball.		Jackie died.
1	2	3

What belongs in box 2?
   Ⓐ Jackie learned that not all people were treated the same.
   Ⓑ Jackie was born.
   Ⓒ Jackie was entered into the Baseball Hall of Fame.
   Ⓓ Jackie joined the Dodgers.

PART ONE: READ A LETTER

Here is a letter written by Gordon. Read the letter.
Then do Numbers 1 through 6.

February 12, 2000

Dear Uncle Nate,

    I wanted to thank you for coming to my school play, <u>Life on the Farm</u>.
You may not know this, but this was the first time I've ever performed in a play.
Boy, was I nervous. When the play started, I could feel my hands sweating and
my heart racing.

    I don't know if you noticed, but I forgot my lines several times. I don't think
anyone heard my teacher whispering them to me across the stage. Did you like
the way I tried to act natural when I tripped over the cows? I think everyone
thought I was supposed to do that.

    The best part was at the end of the play when we took a bow and
everyone clapped.

    Thank you again for coming to my play. I'll let you know when I'm in
another one.

Your nephew,

Gordon

Finding Main Idea

1. The main idea of the first paragraph is found
   - Ⓐ in the first sentence.
   - Ⓑ in the last sentence.
   - Ⓒ in the middle of the paragraph.
   - Ⓓ by thinking about the most important idea in the paragraph.

Recalling Facts and Details

4. Who helped Gordon when he forgot his lines?
   - Ⓐ his uncle
   - Ⓑ his teacher
   - Ⓒ his mother
   - Ⓓ his friend

Finding Main Idea

2. What is the letter mainly about?
   - Ⓐ a nervous nephew
   - Ⓑ a favorite uncle
   - Ⓒ a school play
   - Ⓓ a silly mistake

Understanding Sequence

5. Which of these happened last?
   - Ⓐ The curtain rose.
   - Ⓑ Everyone clapped.
   - Ⓒ Gordon's heart raced.
   - Ⓓ Gordon tripped.

Recalling Facts and Details

3. Which detail tells that Gordon was nervous?
   - Ⓐ I could feel my hands sweating.
   - Ⓑ I tripped over the cows.
   - Ⓒ This was the first time I've ever performed in a play.
   - Ⓓ Thank you for coming to my play.

Understanding Sequence

6. You can tell the order of events described in the letter by
   - Ⓐ thinking about the beginning, the middle, and the ending.
   - Ⓑ looking for clue words.
   - Ⓒ thinking about the main idea.
   - Ⓓ finding the facts and details.

Here is a story about a girl named Johanna. Read the story. Then do Numbers 7 through 12.

The factory whistle blew and woke Johanna. Daddy whistled while he changed the baby. The teakettle whistled when the water was hot. But Johanna could not whistle, although she puckered her lips and tried.

Mommy whistled while she hung the wash on the line to dry. The noon whistle blew, as it did every day. The loon on the lake whistled as it flew away. And Johanna tried to whistle, but the air just blew out of her mouth.

The policeman blew his whistle as he directed the traffic. The train whistled when it approached the crossing. And the bright, red cardinal whistled from the swinging branch of a tree. Johanna sat on her swing and tried to do the same. But however hard she tried, the sound that came out was not a whistle.

The coach of the basketball team at the playground blew her whistle. The wind whistled as it blew around the eaves in the store.

Johanna's big brother whistled as he cleaned his bike. And Johanna tried until she was red in the face.

Aunt Josephine could put a blade of grass between her thumbs and blow, making a most perfect whistling sound. And when Grandpa snored, he sometimes whistled even without puckering up. The big boy next door curled his lip around his teeth and whistled so loudly that everybody frowned. And Johanna—was that a whistle? She puckered her lips and tried again, and yes . . .

Johanna could whistle! Hurrah!

Finding Main Idea

7. What is the main idea of the story?
   - Ⓐ The factory whistle woke Johanna.
   - Ⓑ Birds can be taught to whistle.
   - Ⓒ Johanna learns to whistle.
   - Ⓓ Johanna's face turns red when she tries to whistle.

Recalling Facts and Details

10. When Grandpa snores, he sometimes
    - Ⓐ wakes everybody up.
    - Ⓑ whistles.
    - Ⓒ frowns.
    - Ⓓ giggles.

Finding Main Idea

8. A good title for this story is
   - Ⓐ "Whistle, Johanna."
   - Ⓑ "Aunt Josephine."
   - Ⓒ "The Whistling Teakettle."
   - Ⓓ "The Boy Next Door."

Understanding Sequence

11. The boxes tell some things that happened in the story.

Johanna cannot whistle.	Johanna tried to whistle until she was red in the face.	
1	2	3

What belongs in box 3?
   - Ⓐ Daddy whistled while he changed the baby.
   - Ⓑ The policeman whistled.
   - Ⓒ The noon whistle blew.
   - Ⓓ Johanna learned to whistle.

Recalling Facts and Details

9. Which of these is not true?
   - Ⓐ Daddy whistles while he changes the baby.
   - Ⓑ Johanna finds learning to whistle easy.
   - Ⓒ The lunch whistle blows every day at noon.
   - Ⓓ Johanna's brother whistles as he cleans his bike.

Understanding Sequence

12. Which of these happened first?
    - Ⓐ Johanna sat on her swing and tried to whistle.
    - Ⓑ The loon on the lake whistled.
    - Ⓒ The coach at the playground blew her whistle.
    - Ⓓ The factory whistle woke Johanna.

PART ONE: LEARN ABOUT CAUSE AND EFFECT

Read this story about Dan. As you read, think about one thing that happens to Dan and why.

Dan dressed quickly. He didn't want to miss the school bus. He grabbed his jacket, put on his shoes, and raced out the door. Oops! Dan forgot to tie his shoes! As a result, Dan tripped over his shoelaces and fell to the ground. Poor Dan! At least he didn't miss the bus!

One thing that happens to Dan and why is

What happens: **He fell to the ground**.
Why it happens: **He tripped over his shoelaces**.

What happens and why is called **cause and effect**.
Why something happens is the **cause**. *He tripped over his shoelaces.*
What happens because of the cause is the **effect**. *He fell to the ground.*

★ A cause is the reason that something happens.

★ An effect is what happens as a result of the cause.

★ Clue words such as *so, so that, since, because,* and *if* often signal cause and effect. Other clues words are *reason* and *as a result.*

Read this journal entry written by a boy who lives on a farm. As you read, look for clue words to help you understand what happens and why it happens. Then answer the questions.

January 28

I woke up this morning to two feet of snow. After breakfast, Father and I went out to feed the hungry animals. Since the snow was so deep, we had trouble getting to the barn. The animals must have been thirsty. Their drinking water froze into a solid block because it was so cold. We'll all be glad when spring comes!

1. The cows' drinking water froze because
   Ⓐ it was so cold.
   Ⓑ the snow was so deep.
   Ⓒ the animals were thirsty.
   Ⓓ the animals were hungry.

2. Which clue word or words signals the reason that the boy and his father had trouble getting to the barn?
   Ⓐ because
   Ⓑ as a result
   Ⓒ so
   Ⓓ since

Work with a partner. Talk about your answers to questions 1 and 2. Tell why you chose the answers you did.

Remember: What happens and why is called cause and effect.

★ To find a cause, look for a reason that something happened.
Ask yourself, "*Why* did it happen?"

★ To find an effect, look for a result, or something that happened.
Ask yourself, "*What* happened?"

★ Look for clue words that signal cause and effect, such as *so, so that, since, because, if, reason,* and *as a result.*

Read this article about the annual rings on trees. As you read, ask yourself, "*What* are some things that happen to trees? *Why* do these things happen?" Then answer the questions.

Annual Rings

Have you ever seen a tree that has been cut down? If you have, you probably saw the circles inside the trunk of the tree. These circles are called annual rings. You can tell how old a tree is by counting the rings.

Trees have rings because each year they grow a new layer of wood. This new layer grows beneath the bark. In a year with lots of rain and sunlight, the tree grows faster. The annual ring that year will be thick. If there is little rain or sunlight, the tree grows slower. The annual ring that year will be thin.

3. Why do trees have rings?
   Ⓐ because they grow fast
   Ⓑ because they are often cut down
   Ⓒ because they get lots of rain and sunlight
   Ⓓ because they grow a new layer of wood each year

4. If there is little rain or sunlight, a tree
   Ⓐ grows faster.
   Ⓑ grows slower.
   Ⓒ has no annual ring.
   Ⓓ grows a thick annual ring.

Look at the answer choices for each question. Read why each answer choice is correct or not correct.

3. Why do trees have rings?

Ⓐ because they grow fast

This answer is not correct because trees grow fast if there is lots of rain and sunlight. This answer does not tell about the cause of the rings.

Ⓑ because they are often cut down

This answer is not correct because this does not tell about the cause of the rings. Cutting down trees does not cause rings.

Ⓒ because they get lots of rain and sunlight

This answer is not correct because trees have rings no matter how much rain and sunlight there is. The amount of rain and sun makes the rings either thick or thin, but does not cause the rings.

● because they grow a new layer of wood each year

This answer is correct because it tells the cause of the rings. The second paragraph states "Trees have rings because each year they grow a new layer of wood." The clue word because *helps you recognize a cause and an effect.*

4. If there is little rain or sunlight, a tree

Ⓐ grows faster.

This answer is not correct because a tree grows faster when there is lots of rain and sunlight.

● grows slower.

This answer is correct because the last two sentences explain that when there is little rain or sun, a tree grows slower.

Ⓒ has no annual ring.

This answer is not correct because annual rings grow each year, no matter what the weather is. The ring may be thick or thin, but the tree will grow.

Ⓓ grows a thick annual ring.

This answer is not correct because a tree grows a thick annual ring in a year with lots of rain and sunlight.

Sometimes, there are no clue words to show cause and effect in a reading passage. When there are no clue words, do the following:

★ To find an effect, think about *what* happened.

★ To find a cause, think about *how* or *why* it happened.

★ Think about what you already know about how one thing might cause another thing to happen.

Read this fable by Aesop. Then answer the questions.

The Boy Who Cried Wolf

There once was a boy who lived in a small village. Each day, he took his sheep to a high meadow to eat grass. One day, the boy decided to play a trick. "Wolf! Wolf!" he cried. "A wolf is here!"

The people in the village rushed to the meadow to save the boy and his sheep. They found the boy safe and laughing. "I was only kidding," the boy said. "There is no wolf here," he laughed.

"You are very naughty," the people said.

The next day, the boy played the same trick. And, once again, the people rushed to the meadow only to find the boy laughing.

A few days passed. The boy was in the meadow, when he saw a real wolf. "Wolf! Wolf!" he cried. "A wolf is getting the sheep."

The people in the village heard the boy's cries. This time, they did not rush to help the boy. They weren't going to be tricked again.

5. The boy took the sheep to the meadow so that they could
   Ⓐ eat grass.
   Ⓑ run in the meadow.
   Ⓒ sleep in the grass.
   Ⓓ play in the meadow.

6. Why did the boy cry "wolf" the first time?
   Ⓐ He saw a wolf.
   Ⓑ He was doing his job.
   Ⓒ He needed help.
   Ⓓ He wanted to play a trick.

7. The people did not come the last time the boy cried "wolf" because they
   Ⓐ were too busy working.
   Ⓑ thought it was another trick.
   Ⓒ did not hear the boy.
   Ⓓ were afraid of the wolf.

8. Why did the people say that the boy was naughty?
   Ⓐ They didn't like to laugh.
   Ⓑ They didn't like funny jokes.
   Ⓒ They didn't like his trick.
   Ⓓ They didn't like the boy.

Read this article about two kinds of simple machines. Then answer the questions.

The Wheel and the Axle

Simple machines are useful because they help people do things that they could not do on their own. The wheel and the axle are two simple machines.

In a car, four wheels help move the car forward and backward. The steering wheel inside the car turns the two front wheels. When a driver turns the steering wheel to the right, the wheels of the car turn to the right. When the driver turns the steering wheel to the left, the wheels of the car turn to the left.

Many wheels, like the four wheels of a car, have a bar that is attached to the center of the wheel. This bar is called an axle. The axle causes the wheels to spin. Skateboards have axles. So do roller skates and bicycles. Look around you. Think about the simple machines that help you do things that you could not do on your own.

9. What causes the front wheels of a car to turn?
   A the engine
   B the steering wheel
   C the axle
   D a bar

10. Simple machines are useful because they
    A cause people to do things they would not usually do.
    B move the front wheels of a car.
    C help people do things they could not do on their own.
    D help wheels turn and spin.

11. What happens when a driver turns the steering wheel to the left?
    A The tires spin.
    B The front wheels turn to the right.
    C The car moves backward.
    D The front wheels turn to the left.

12. The part of a car that causes the wheels to spin is called the
    A axle.
    B front wheel.
    C steering wheel.
    D driver.

★ A test question about cause and effect may ask you *what* happened in a reading passage.

★ A test question about cause and effect may ask you *why* something happened.

★ A test question about cause and effect often contains words such as *because, why, reason,* or *what happened.*

Here is a letter written by Juan. Read the letter. Then do Numbers 13 and 14.

September 29, 2000

Dear Ms. Frutt,

I have made an important decision. I have decided to quit third grade and return to your class.

It's not that I don't like third grade. The kids are friendly, and my new teacher, Mr. Lee, is nice. He lets us do experiments in class and tells funny jokes. He also lets us have a snake for a class pet.

The problem is that third grade is not as much fun as second grade. The work is harder, and we have homework every night. We have a math test every Friday, and we have to write a book report every other month. Besides, I miss my two best friends from last year. We were all together in your class. We are now in different classrooms. I miss second grade. So, I'll see you back in second grade on Monday morning.

Your student from last year,
Juan

Recognizing Cause and Effect

13. One reason that Juan wants to quit third grade is that
    Ⓐ he misses Ms. Frutt.
    Ⓑ the work is harder.
    Ⓒ the kids aren't friendly.
    Ⓓ he doesn't like doing experiments.

Recognizing Cause and Effect

14. What happened to Juan's two best friends?
    Ⓐ They each went to Mr. Lee's classroom.
    Ⓑ They each went to a different school.
    Ⓒ They each went to a different classroom.
    Ⓓ They each moved to another city.

Here is an article about travel in a land full of snow and ice.
Read the article. Then do Numbers 15 and 16.

Winters are long in the Arctic. People who live there cannot grow crops on the frozen earth. They must find animals and fish to eat. Arctic hunters and fishers must travel across snow and ice.

Long ago, Arctic people learned how to build sleds. They built sleds with runners. Runners are blades on the bottom of a sled. The runners moved easily over the hard-packed snow. The runners were usually made out of wood. But few trees grow in the Arctic. Strips of animal bones and horns were added to make the wooden runners stronger. The Arctic people trained dogs to pull the sleds.

Today, people of the Arctic still hunt and fish. But snowmobiles have become more popular than sleds. Snowmobiles can go faster than sleds pulled by animals. Snowmobiles don't get tired or need to rest!

Recognizing Cause and Effect

15. Bones and horns were added to runners because they
   Ⓐ made it easier for dogs to pull the sleds.
   Ⓑ helped the runners move across the snow.
   Ⓒ caused the sled to go faster.
   Ⓓ made the runners stronger.

Recognizing Cause and Effect

16. Why are snowmobiles more popular than sleds?
   Ⓐ There are few trees to build sleds.
   Ⓑ Snowmobiles go faster than sleds.
   Ⓒ There are no animals to pull the sleds.
   Ⓓ Snowmobiles hold more people than sleds.

STRATEGY 5

PART ONE: LEARN ABOUT COMPARING AND CONTRASTING

Read this journal entry written by Jake. As you read, think about the ways Jake and his friend Alex are alike and the ways they are different.

October 15, 2000

I sometimes wonder why Alex and I are friends. Alex has a great personality (like me!) and he's funny (like me!), but sometimes I don't understand him one bit.

Alex showed up at school today wearing the most horrible clothes. He doesn't care at all what he looks like. Me? I like to look good. Not Alex. He'll wear anything.

Then there are Alex's eating habits! Put it on a plate and put it in front of him, and Alex will eat it. He'll eat anything! Me? I care about what I eat. I try to eat healthful foods. I like broccoli pizza the best. But hold the milk. Better yet, give it to Alex. He'll love it!

Ways in which Jake and Alex are alike:

Both have a great personality.
Both are funny.

Ways in which Jake and Alex are different:

Jake cares about what he wears, but Alex does not.
Jake cares about what he eats, but Alex will eat anything.

Finding how two or more things are alike and how they are different is called **comparing and contrasting**. Comparing is finding how things are alike. Contrasting is finding how things are different.

★ Clue words that signal how things are alike are *same*, *like*, and *alike*.

★ Clue words that signal how things are different are *but*, *unlike*, *different*, and *however*.

★ People, places, objects, and events can all be compared and contrasted.

Day 2

Read this passage about Russia. As you read, look for clue words that tell how Russia is like other countries and how it is different. Then answer the questions.

Russia is the largest country in the world. Canada is the second largest country in the world. Russia is almost twice as large as Canada.

Russia is unlike most other countries. It is one of the few countries that is on two continents. One part of Russia is in Europe. The other part is in Asia. When people at one end of Russia are waking up, people at the other end are going to bed.

Because it is so large, Russia has many different climates. In much of Russia, however, winter is the longest season. In the northern part of the country, cold weather can last for eight months. Winters there are dark and cold. There are many snowstorms. Sometimes people cannot leave their houses for days and days. Few people live in this part of Russia.

1. How are Russia and Canada alike?
   Ⓐ Both have a warm climate.
   ● Both are large countries.
   Ⓒ Both are in Asia.
   Ⓓ Both are on two continents.

2. Which clue word signals how Russia is different from other countries?
   Ⓐ but
   Ⓑ same
   ● unlike
   Ⓓ however

 Work with a partner. Talk about your answers to questions 1 and 2. Tell why you chose the answers you did.

Remember: Comparing is finding ways that things are alike.
Contrasting is finding ways that things are different.

★ To compare, look for clue words that signal a likeness, such as *same, like,* and *alike.*

★ To contrast, look for clue words that signal a difference, such as *but, unlike, different,* and *however.*

★ Look for people, places, objects, and events that are being compared and contrasted.

Read this article that Todd wrote for a student newspaper.
As you read, look for how things are alike and how they are different.
Then answer the questions.

Skating in Hilltown

Most people were excited when the new indoor ice-skating rink opened last year. Before the rink was built, most people skated at the pond. But they could skate only in winter, when the water froze.

The people of Hilltown can now skate year-round. The Hilltown Rink is open from eight in the morning until eight at night. Most people say that they like skating at the new rink better than at the pond.

I guess I'm not like most people. I like skating at the pond. Sure, the ice is bumpy, unlike the smooth surface of the rink. And it does get pretty chilly. But I love the freedom of skating outside. On the pond, we can play hockey anytime. However, at the rink, only teams can play hockey.

The best part of the pond is the price. Skating at the pond is free. At the rink, skating costs five dollars!

3. In what way are the pond and the skating rink alike?
   Ⓐ Both are bumpy.
   Ⓑ Both are indoors.
   Ⓒ Both are open until eight at night.
   Ⓓ Both are used for skating.

4. Which clue word signals how playing hockey at the rink is different from playing hockey at the pond?
   Ⓐ like
   Ⓑ unlike
   Ⓒ however
   Ⓓ different

Look at the answer choices for each question. Read why each answer choice is correct or not correct.

3. In what way are the pond and the skating rink alike?

   Ⓐ Both are bumpy.

   This answer is not correct because the third paragraph states that the ice at the pond is bumpy, not smooth like the surface of the rink.

   Ⓑ Both are indoors.

   This answer is not correct because a pond is found outdoors, not indoors.

   Ⓒ Both are open until eight at night.

   This answer is not correct because nothing in the article tells about the hours that the pond is open for skating.

   ● Both are used for skating.

   This answer is correct because people can skate at both places.

4. Which clue word signals how playing hockey at the rink is different from playing hockey at the pond?

   Ⓐ like

   This answer is not correct because the word like *signals that things are alike, not different.*

   Ⓑ unlike

   This answer is not correct because the word unlike *is used in the third paragraph to tell how the surface of the pond is different from the surface of the rink: "Sure, the ice is bumpy, unlike the smooth surface of the rink."*

   ● however

   This answer is correct because the third paragraph states "On the pond, we can play hockey anytime. However, at the rink, only teams can play hockey."

   Ⓓ different

   This answer is not correct because this word is not used in the article.

Sometimes, there are no clue words in a reading passage to signal how things are alike or how they are different. When there are no clue words,

★ think about the people, places, objects, or events that you read about. Ask yourself, "How are they alike?"

★ think about the people, places, objects, or events that you read about. Ask yourself, "How are they different?"

Read this article about two planets. Then answer the questions.

Jupiter and Earth

Nine planets travel around our sun. Earth is one of these planets. Earth is the third closest planet to the sun. Jupiter is the fifth closest planet to the sun.

Jupiter is like a giant compared to Earth. It is the size of 1,000 Earths. Earth turns around once every 24 hours. Jupiter turns around in less than ten hours. It takes 12 years for Jupiter to go around the sun one time. It takes Earth 365 days to go around the sun one time.

Jupiter is covered by an ocean. Scientists believe the ocean may be 10,000 miles deep! But forget about swimming. You might get cold in your swimsuit. The temperature on Jupiter is much colder than that on Earth. On Jupiter, it is more than 250°F below freezing!

5. How is Jupiter different from Earth?
   Ⓐ Jupiter is larger than Earth.
   Ⓑ Jupiter is closer to the sun than Earth.
   Ⓒ Jupiter does not travel around the sun.
   Ⓓ Jupiter is warmer than Earth.

6. In what way are Jupiter and Earth alike?
   Ⓐ Both are small.
   Ⓑ Both turn around in ten hours.
   Ⓒ Both travel around the sun.
   Ⓓ Both are the same size.

7. In the article, Jupiter is compared to
   Ⓐ the sun.
   Ⓑ a star.
   Ⓒ a planet.
   Ⓓ a giant.

8. The temperature on Jupiter is
   Ⓐ warmer than Earth's.
   Ⓑ colder than Earth's.
   Ⓒ the same as Earth's.
   Ⓓ hotter than Earth's.

Read this story about two sisters. Then answer the questions.

"I'll never be as good a basketball player as you," Sam said. She slammed the basketball to the ground. "Never."

Jen, Sam's sister, picked up the ball. "That's not true. If you practice, you will get better. You already know how to dribble and how to pass and shoot. That's more than I knew at your age."

"Really?" Sam questioned. She wasn't convinced.

Jen nodded. "Yes, *really*. When I was eight years old, all I could do was shoot. And I couldn't even do that very well. I'm fourteen now. I've played six more years than you have. I've been on four different teams and practice three days a week. Once you join your team next week, you'll get better. It just happens." With that, Jen picked up the ball and tossed it to her sister.

Sam opened her arms to catch the ball. "I guess I better keep practicing," she said with a grin.

9. One way that Sam and Jen are alike is that they both
   Ⓐ are going to join a basketball team next week.
   Ⓑ like to play basketball.
   Ⓒ have played basketball for six years.
   Ⓓ want to be better basketball players.

10. One thing that Jen could do at age eight that Sam can also do is
    Ⓐ practice.
    Ⓑ dribble.
    Ⓒ pass.
    Ⓓ shoot.

11. Which of these tells one difference between Sam and Jen?
    Ⓐ Sam does not play basketball as well as Jen.
    Ⓑ Sam has been playing basketball longer than Jen has.
    Ⓒ Sam likes basketball more than Jen does.
    Ⓓ Sam practices more than Jen.

12. Which of these is true?
    Ⓐ Jen plays many sports, and Sam does not.
    Ⓑ Jen has played on fewer teams than Sam.
    Ⓒ Jen is older than Sam.
    Ⓓ Jen will always be a better player than Sam.

★ A test question about comparing, or likenesses, usually contains clue words such as *same, like,* or *alike.*

★ A test question about contrasting, or differences, usually contains clue words such as *different, unlike,* or *not like.*

Here is an article about bears. Read the article. Then do Numbers 13 and 14.

There are about seven types of bears throughout the world. Only two types live in the wild forests of North America. These are the black bear and the brown bear.

Both of these large mammals live in forests. Both are also covered with fur and have big heads, short legs, and strong tails.

About 80,000 American black bears live in the northern forests of North America. They have black or dark-brown fur. Most American black bears grow to be five or six feet long and weigh up to 350 pounds. They are shy, and they usually hide from people.

There are a few thousand brown bears that live in the western forests of North America. Most brown bears have brown fur. Some have white fur mixed in with the brown fur. These bears are called "grizzly bears." Most brown bears grow to be about nine feet long and weigh up to 1,700 pounds. These bears are not shy. In fact, they can anger quickly and are known to chase people!

Comparing and Contrasting

13. How are black bears and brown bears alike?
   Ⓐ Both are shy.
   Ⓑ Both are short.
   Ⓒ Both live in forests.
   Ⓓ Both weigh about 350 pounds.

Comparing and Contrasting

14. One way that black bears are not like brown bears is that black bears
   Ⓐ are not found in North America but brown bears are.
   Ⓑ are dark brown and brown bears are white.
   Ⓒ grow to be longer than brown bears.
   Ⓓ hide from people and brown bears do not.

Here is Eve's science report about two kinds of storms. Read the report. Then do Numbers 15 and 16.

Eve Thomas   Grade 3

Two Kinds of Storms

Tornadoes are storms that form over land. Most tornadoes happen in the middle of the United States. Tornado winds can blow up to 300 miles per hour. Tornadoes don't travel far, usually no more than 20 miles. In the United States, tornado season is from March until August.

Hurricanes are storms that form over the ocean. Most hurricanes happen in places along the coast. Hurricanes also have strong winds, but not as strong as a tornado's. These storms can travel for hundreds of miles. In the United States, hurricane season is from June to November.

Tornadoes usually last a matter of minutes. Hurricanes can last for days. However, hurricanes usually don't cause as much damage as tornadoes.

Comparing and Contrasting

15. Which of these tells how a tornado is different from a hurricane?

Ⓐ A tornado lasts longer.

Ⓑ A tornado travels farther.

Ⓒ A tornado usually causes more damage.

Ⓓ A tornado can last for weeks.

Comparing and Contrasting

16. How are a tornado and a hurricane the same?

Ⓐ They both form over the ocean.

Ⓑ They both occur from March until April.

Ⓒ They both occur only in the middle of the United States.

Ⓓ They both are storms with strong winds.

PART ONE: LEARN ABOUT MAKING PREDICTIONS

Read the first part of this story about a boy named Ty. As you read, think about what might happen next in the story.

Birthday Surprise

Ty loves animals. He has always wanted a pet of his own. Every year, Ty asks his parents for a puppy. "Wait until you're 12," they always say. Today is Ty's birthday. He is 12 years old.

Think about what you read and what you already know about birthdays. Make a good guess about what might happen next. Then, continue reading to see how close your guess is to what actually happens.

Ty went down to the kitchen. His mother gave him a big birthday hug. Ty looked around the room. "No puppy," he said to himself. Ty's head hung low as he started to leave the room. Just then, he heard a bark. A black-and-white puppy ran in from the living room.

What happened next in the story was **Ty got a puppy for his birthday.**

When you think about what might happen next in a reading passage, you are **making a prediction**. Making a prediction is a way of using clues from a reading passage, as well as things you already know, to make a good guess about what might happen next.

★ Clues are often in the title of a reading passage. Read the title, and then make a prediction about what you will be reading.

★ Clues are often in the facts and details in a reading passage. Details about the things characters do and say often help you make a prediction about what they might do or say later in the story.

★ Clues are often in any pictures included with a story. Pictures often show something that is happening or will happen soon.

Read this story about story hour at a library. As you read, ask yourself, "What does the title tell me about what I will be reading? Which facts and details will help me predict what will happen next?" Then answer the questions.

Story Hour

Miss Dee is the storyteller at the library. Today, she is getting ready to read a new book. The children are seated on the floor around her storytelling chair.

"Does anyone here have a pet?" Miss Dee asked.

Billy raised his hand and told everyone about his cat, Snowball. Marta told a story about Rover, her dog. Liz talked about her goldfish, Bubbles.

Miss Dee asked the children if they knew anyone who had a pet dinosaur.

"No one could have a pet dinosaur!" Marta laughed.

"Well, let's see," said Miss Dee as she took a large picture book out of the bag next to her chair.

1. Which of these is most likely the name of the book that Miss Dee will read?
   Ⓐ *Trains and Planes*
   Ⓑ *Princess Polly Goes to Paris*
   Ⓒ *Taking T. rex for a Walk*
   Ⓓ *Pioneer Family*

2. Where did you find clues to help you make your prediction?
   Ⓐ in the title of the story
   Ⓑ in the things Miss Dee said
   Ⓒ in the details about the pets of other children
   Ⓓ in the details about what Miss Dee took out of her bag

 Work with a partner. Talk about your answers to questions 1 and 2. Tell why you chose the answers you did.

Remember: Making a prediction is a way of using clues from a reading passage, as well as things you already know, to make a good guess about what might happen next.

★ Look for clues in the details of a reading passage to help you make a good guess about what might happen next. Clues are often in the title, in the facts and details, and in any pictures.

★ Ask yourself, "What do I already know about the things I am reading about?"

Read this article about a popular author. As you read, think about the kind of books the author writes. Then answer the questions.

Have you ever met Brave Irene, Dr. DeSoto, or Sylvester the donkey? If you have, then you have probably read the books of William Steig.

William Steig began his career as a cartoonist. When Steig was 22, his father told him the family needed money. Steig thought drawing cartoons would be an easy way to earn some money. He was right! He soon sold a cartoon to the *New Yorker* magazine. Steig has had a cartoon in the *New Yorker* almost every week for the past 60 years. That's close to 3,000 cartoons!

Steig wrote his first children's book in 1969. He has since written many more books for children. The heroes of Steig's books are brave, clever, and full of hope. They are also very amusing. Ask your school librarian for books by William Steig. You'll be glad you did!

William and Jeanne Steig

3. The hero of William Steig's next children's book probably will be
   Ⓐ silly and stupid.
   Ⓑ tired and grumpy.
   Ⓒ lazy and foolish.
   Ⓓ smart and funny.

4. Which detail from the article helped you make your prediction?
   Ⓐ The heroes of Steig's books are brave, clever, and full of hope.
   Ⓑ Ask your school librarian for books by William Steig.
   Ⓒ William Steig began his career as a cartoonist.
   Ⓓ He has since written many more books for children.

Look at the answer choices for each question. Read why each answer choice is correct or not correct.

3. The hero of William Steig's next children's book probably will be

   Ⓐ silly and stupid.

   This answer is not correct because the last paragraph tells you that the heroes in Steig's book are brave, clever, and full of hope.

   Ⓑ tired and grumpy.

   This answer is not correct because the last paragraph tells about the kind of heroes in Steig's books. A hero probably would not be tired and grumpy.

   Ⓒ lazy and foolish.

   This answer is not correct because the last paragraph tells that the heroes in Steig's book are brave, clever, and full of hope. A hero who was lazy and foolish probably would not be in one of his books.

   ● smart and funny.

   This answer is correct because the last paragraph tells about the kind of heroes in Steig's books. Since some heroes are clever and amusing, a hero who was smart and funny probably would be in one of his books.

4. Which detail from the article helped you make your prediction?

   ● The heroes of Steig's books are brave, clever, and full of hope.

   This answer is correct because this detail helps you predict what kind of characters might be in future books.

   Ⓑ Ask your school librarian for books by William Steig.

   This answer is not correct because this detail does not give any clues about the kinds of characters Steig writes about.

   Ⓒ William Steig began his career as a cartoonist.

   This answer is not correct because this detail gives a clue only about one of Steig's other talents.

   Ⓓ He has since written many more books for children.

   This answer is not correct because this detail gives a clue only about the number of books Steig has written.

★ Think about what you already know about the things described in a reading passage. If you are reading about weather, think about what you already know about weather. If you are reading about a pet, think about what you already know about pets.

★ Link what you already know with the clues you find in the reading passage to make a good prediction.

Read this article about two brothers fishing on a lake. Then answer the questions.

"Look at the sky," Pablo said as he cast his fishing line from the front seat of the canoe.

His brother, Diego, glanced upward. The bright sunlight of the morning sky was gone. In its place were dark clouds, moving swiftly across the blue sky. "Where did all of those clouds come from?"

Pablo shrugged. "I don't know, but they sure moved in quickly." Pablo looked over his shoulder. The clouds were turning darker. "It looks like the weather is going to change."

"I agree," Diego said. A strong, warm breeze blew across his face. He tightened the cap on his head. "I wonder how long we should stay out on the lake."

As Diego spoke, a flash of light lit up the sky. "I don't know about you," Pablo replied, "but I think we should head home *now!*"

5. Predict what kind of weather will most likely occur next.
   Ⓐ The sky will become sunny again.
   Ⓑ Snow will fall on the lake.
   Ⓒ Cold winds will blow across the lake and hail will start to fall.
   Ⓓ Rain will fall from the dark clouds.

6. What will the boys most likely do next?
   Ⓐ stay on the lake
   Ⓑ paddle to shore
   Ⓒ talk more about what to do
   Ⓓ yell for help

7. Predict what would happen if the boys stayed on the lake.
   Ⓐ They would catch many fish.
   Ⓑ The would fall out of the canoe.
   Ⓒ They would be in danger from the storm.
   Ⓓ The weather would clear.

8. If the weather had not changed, the boys would probably have
   Ⓐ gone swimming.
   Ⓑ returned home.
   Ⓒ continued fishing.
   Ⓓ gotten into an argument.

Read this article about an unusual pet. Then answer the questions.

House Rabbits

A house rabbit is just that—a rabbit that lives in your house instead of outside or in a barn. You can even have an apartment rabbit. Rabbits are great pets because they like to be around people and are very friendly and affectionate.

A rabbit that lives inside needs its own hutch. A hutch is a small rabbit house made of wire and wood.

Rabbits are very smart and very clean. Like a cat, a rabbit can learn to use a litter box. Put a litter box inside the rabbit's hutch. In just a few weeks, the rabbit will figure out how to use it.

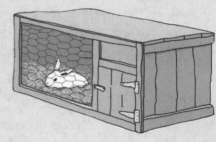

Rabbits are very curious, and they love to chew. They will chew anything! Before you let your rabbit loose in your house, give it a safe toy to chew.

9. Predict what would happen if you placed a toy rabbit outside the hutch near your pet rabbit.
   A The rabbit would ignore it.
   B The rabbit would sleep with it.
   C The rabbit would show interest in it.
   D The rabbit would be afraid of it.

10. If you were going to buy a pet rabbit, which book would probably be most useful?
    A *All About Wild Rabbits*
    B *Caring for Pet Rabbits*
    C *Floppy Bunny Goes to School*
    D *How to Train Your Pet*

11. Predict what would most likely happen if you did not provide safe toys for your pet rabbit to chew.
    A The rabbit would run away.
    B The rabbit would find something else to chew.
    C The rabbit would lose its teeth in time.
    D The rabbit would soon stop eating.

12. Who would most likely buy a pet rabbit?
    A Someone who doesn't like cats.
    B Someone who has a big yard.
    C Someone who lives in an apartment.
    D Someone who wants a loving pet.

★ A test question about making a prediction may ask you to make a good guess about what will happen next in a reading passage, or what might happen in the future.

★ A test question about making a prediction usually contains the words *predict, probably,* or *most likely.*

Here is an article about birds. Read the article. Then do Numbers 13 and 14.

Be Kind to Your Feathered Friends

Many birds in the wild depend on the kindness of people for their food. This is especially true in places where there are many homes and roads. When land is cleared to build new neighborhoods, many plants are destroyed. That makes it harder for birds to find food. If people don't provide food, the birds must find a new place to live.

There are several different ways to feed birds. One way is to put out a feeder filled with sunflower seeds or mixed seeds. Cardinals like to eat from a feeder. Other birds, like sparrows, prefer to eat seeds that have been scattered on the ground. In the winter months, birds need fat to help them survive the cold. To help them, take a large pine cone, spread it with peanut butter, and then roll the cone in mixed seed. Add a string hanger, and place it on a tree branch. Try one of these ideas, or try them all. Don't be surprised if it takes a while for the birds to find the food. But once they do, they'll keep coming back for more.

Making Predictions

13. Predict what will probably happen the day after you hang a new bird feeder.

Ⓐ The seeds will sprout new plants.

Ⓑ Few, if any, birds will eat from it.

Ⓒ Sparrows will scatter the seeds to the ground.

Ⓓ Birds will enjoy the food within minutes of hanging the feeder.

Making Predictions

14. What would most likely happen if people stopped providing food for wild birds?

Ⓐ The birds would have to find different foods to eat.

Ⓑ The birds would die.

Ⓒ The birds would move to another area.

Ⓓ The birds would begin to eat other animals.

Here is a story about two cousins in an unusual situation. Read the story. Then do Numbers 15 and 16.

Lin felt uneasy as she stood on the pitcher's mound. She could scarcely look at the batter, her cousin David. Though they had played baseball together many times at the park, Lin had never before pitched to David in a real game. At the park, David usually swung and missed whenever Lin pitched to him.

"Should I pitch easier to David than I have to the other players?" Lin wondered. "After all, he is my cousin. I would feel terrible if I struck him out, especially in front of all his friends."

Lin took a deep breath. Perhaps the idea of throwing easy pitches was not so good. "David and I have played baseball so often," Lin said to herself, "he'll know if I don't pitch my best. He would be upset if he thought I was taking it easy on him. Besides, he got two hits against the other pitcher. Maybe he can do the same against me." Lin's doubt was brief. She knew what she had to do.

Making Predictions

15. Predict what Lin will do next.
   Ⓐ She will throw the ball harder than she ever has.
   Ⓑ She will ask her coach to get another pitcher.
   Ⓒ She will pitch easily to her cousin.
   Ⓓ She will pitch to her cousin as she would to any other batter.

Making Predictions

16. What will most likely happen if Lin pitches to David the way she usually does?
   Ⓐ David will hit a home run.
   Ⓑ David will strike out.
   Ⓒ David will swing only at the slow pitches.
   Ⓓ David will hit the ball farther than he ever has.

PART ONE: READ AN ARTICLE

Here is an article about a different kind of school. Read the article. Then do Numbers 1 through 6.

Long ago, there were few schools in the United States. Most children learned to read and write at home. As towns and villages got bigger, people began to build schoolhouses.

Many early schoolhouses had only one room. So, students of all ages were in the same class. Students who were six years old studied next to students who were 12 or 13 years old.

A one-room schoolhouse had only one teacher. Most teachers were just a few years older than some of their students. The teacher sat at a high desk in the front of the class. This way, the teacher could see over the entire room.

A wood stove in the middle of the room provided heat. Students brought in wood from home. The walls of the classroom were black and sooty because of the smoke of the stove.

One hundred years ago, there were about 200,000 one-room schoolhouses in the United States. Today, there are only about 800. They are located in parts of the country where few people live. Alaska and parts of California are home to many of today's one-room schoolhouses.

Recognizing Cause and Effect

1. Why did teachers in a one-room schoolhouse sit at a high desk?
   - (A) Most of them were small children.
   - (B) They wanted to be able to see the whole room.
   - (C) They wanted to be treated like kings and queens.
   - (D) They wanted students to be able to see them.

Comparing and Contrasting

4. How are one-room schoolhouses like most large schools today?
   - (A) Both are heated with wood stoves.
   - (B) Both are places for learning.
   - (C) Both have children of all ages in one class.
   - (D) Both have only one room.

Recognizing Cause and Effect

2. Which clue word signals the reason that the walls of a one-room schoolhouse were black?
   - (A) so
   - (B) since
   - (C) reason
   - (D) because

Making Predictions

5. Predict where you would most likely find a one-room schoolhouse today.
   - (A) in the city
   - (B) in a small town
   - (C) near an amusement park
   - (D) close to busy shopping areas

Comparing and Contrasting

3. Teachers in one-room schoolhouses of the past were different from teachers today because they
   - (A) sat at a desk.
   - (B) taught students in heated rooms.
   - (C) lived and worked at the school.
   - (D) taught students of all ages in the same room.

Making Predictions

6. An old one-room schoolhouse has been turned into a museum. Predict what you would most likely find in the museum.
   - (A) a book about computers
   - (B) a model of a spaceship
   - (C) a classroom filled with children
   - (D) a box filled with chopped wood

Here is a folktale from China. Read the folktale.
Then do Numbers 7 through 12.

The Painter and the Judge

Once there was a judge who was very mean. Everyone knew that to get him to listen to you, you had to go to him secretly and give him huge amounts of money. And even then he might just take the money and still not give you a fair hearing. People often felt that he had cheated them.

One day the judge heard there was a painter in town who could paint the most wonderful pictures. The judge found the man and gave him a roll of white paper to get working on.

"Paint me a beautiful picture," said the judge.

At first the painter didn't want to. He knew how mean the judge was and said to himself, "I might do a lot of work on this painting and end up not getting paid."

"I'm very busy at the moment," he said. "I just don't have the time."

But the judge begged him, saying, "I shall put it up where all the most important people in town will see it."

In the end the painter said he would do a picture for the judge.

The next day, he came to the judge's house with the roll of paper.

"Wise One, I have finished the painting."

The judge was delighted, but when he unrolled the paper, he couldn't see any picture on it. Instead, there were a few words: "Cows on Grass."

The judge stared at the blank piece of paper.

"But where's the grass?" he said.

"The cows have eaten it," answered the painter.

"But then where are the cows?" said the judge.

"Well," said the painter, "seeing as they'd eaten all the grass, there wasn't much point in their hanging around any longer, was there? So they left."

Recognizing Cause and Effect

7. At first, the painter did not want to paint a picture for the judge because
   (A) he didn't have any paint.
   (B) he couldn't think of anything to paint a picture of.
   (C) he thought the judge might not pay him.
   (D) he was too busy doing work for someone else.

Recognizing Cause and Effect

8. Why did the painter agree to paint a picture for the judge?
   (A) because the judge promised to hang the picture where important people would see it
   (B) because the judge paid the painter a handsome sum
   (C) because the painter feared the judge
   (D) because the painter decided he did have time after all

Comparing and Contrasting

9. How was the judge in the folktale different from most judges?
   (A) He liked to listen to people.
   (B) He was rich.
   (C) He liked art.
   (D) He cheated people.

Comparing and Contrasting

10. How was the painting that the painter gave the judge different from most paintings?
    (A) It had no pictures on it.
    (B) It had real grass on it.
    (C) It showed cows eating grass.
    (D) It told a story.

Making Predictions

11. What would a man most likely do if he wanted the judge to listen to him?
    (A) paint the judge a picture
    (B) offer the judge lots of money
    (C) write the judge a letter
    (D) cheat the judge out of money

Making Predictions

12. Predict what would probably happen the next time that the judge wants a painting.
    (A) He will try to paint the picture himself.
    (B) He will ask the same painter to do the work.
    (C) He will hire a different painter.
    (D) He will pay the painter huge amounts of money.

PART ONE: LEARN ABOUT FINDING WORD MEANING IN CONTEXT

Read this story about Paul and his grandfather. As you read, think about the meaning of the word *launch* in the last sentence.

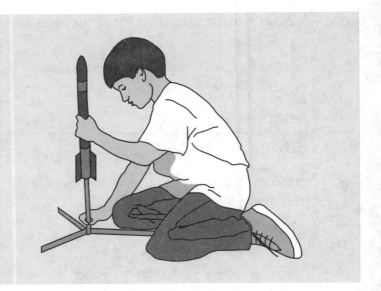

Paul and his grandfather build rockets together. Today they are going to try out the new rocket they made. Paul placed the rocket in the middle of the yard. Grandfather handed Paul the controls to the rocket.

"When you're ready to send the rocket into space, push the red button," said Grandfather. Paul smiled as he got ready to launch the rocket.

You can figure out the meaning of the word *launch* by looking at the words and phrases around it. The word *rocket* and the phrase *send into space* are clues to the meaning of the word *launch*.

The meaning of the word *launch* is "to send a rocket into space."

When you use clues in a reading passage to figure out the meaning of a new word, you are **finding word meaning in context**. The words and phrases around a new word often provide clues to the word's meaning. These clues are called **context clues**.

★ Context clues are often in the sentence where the new word appears. They can also be in the sentences before and after the word.

★ Clues about the meaning of a new word are often found by thinking about the way the word is used in the sentence.

★ Clues about the meaning of a new word can be found by thinking about the facts and details in the paragraph where the new word is found.

Read this poem about a butterfly. As you read, ask yourself, "What clues will I use to figure out the meaning of the word *hovering*?" Then answer the questions.

> **Butterfly Song**
> Butterfly, butterfly, butterfly, butterfly
> Oh, look, see it hovering among the flowers,
> It is like a baby trying to walk and not knowing how to go.
> The clouds sprinkle down the rain.

1. The word *hovering* probably means
   Ⓐ "smelling the flowers."
   Ⓑ "soaring through the air."
   Ⓒ "looking for flowers."
   Ⓓ "staying in one place."

2. Which phrase gives a clue to the meaning of the word *hovering*?
   Ⓐ butterfly, butterfly, butterfly
   Ⓑ look, see it
   Ⓒ like a baby trying to walk
   Ⓓ sprinkle down the rain

 Work with a partner. Talk about your answers to questions 1 and 2. Tell why you chose the answers you did.

Remember: The words and phrases around a new word often give clues about the word's meaning.

★ Look for context clues in the sentence where the word appears. Look also in sentences before and after the new word.

★ Look for clues about the meaning of a new word by thinking about the way the word is used in the sentence.

★ Look for clues about the meaning of a new word by thinking about the facts and details in the paragraph where the new word is found.

Read this modern fairy tale. As you read, think about how you will figure out the meaning of any new words. Then answer the questions.

The New Princess

Once upon a time, there was a king and a queen. They were excited about the birth of their daughter. Fairies flew in from all directions to see the new princess.

The fairies looked at the sleeping baby. As they began to bestow beauty, charm, and grace upon her, they said, "Our gifts will help the princess become beautiful, charming, and graceful."

"Wait a minute!" announced the queen. "Of course, I want my daughter to be beautiful, charming, and graceful. But most of all, I want her to be herself. If she wants to be charming, let her practice her manners. If she wants to be smart, she can study. If she wants to be musical, let her take music lessons."

And so, with no help from the fairies, the princess grew into a lovely young lady. All in all, everyone thought she turned out pretty well.

3. In paragraph two, the word *bestow* probably means
   Ⓐ "to look for."
   Ⓑ "to cover with."
   Ⓒ "to take away."
   Ⓓ "to give as a gift."

4. What is the best meaning of the word *charming* in the story?
   Ⓐ "most beautiful of all"
   Ⓑ "protected from harm"
   Ⓒ "pleasing and polite to others"
   Ⓓ "acting rudely"

Look at the answer choices for each question. Read why each answer choice is correct or not correct.

3. In paragraph two, the word *bestow* probably means

   Ⓐ "to look for."

   This answer is not correct because the fairies did not come to the castle to look for something.

   Ⓑ "to cover with."

   This answer is not correct because the words and phrases around the word do not give any clues about the baby's being covered with anything.

   Ⓒ "to take away."

   This answer is not correct because there are no clues that say that fairies took something from the baby.

   ● "to give as a gift."

   This answer is correct because the words and phrases before and after the word tell about the fairies coming to the castle to bring gifts. You can figure out that the word bestow probably means, "to give as a gift."

4. What is the best meaning of the word *charming* in the story?

   Ⓐ "most beautiful of all"

   This answer is not correct because the words and phrases around the word tell that in order to be charming one would have to practice manners. Being the most beautiful of all has nothing to do with being charming.

   Ⓑ "protected from harm"

   This answer is not correct because the words and phrases around the word do not describe anything that would protect the baby from harm.

   ● "pleasing and polite to others"

   This answer is correct because the phrase "let her practice her manners" is near the word charming. *The phrase gives a clue about the word's meaning. You can figure out that someone who has good manners is probably pleasing and polite to others.*

   Ⓓ "acting rudely"

   This answer is not correct because the words and phrases around the word do not describe ways of acting badly or rudely.

★ Look for a synonym, a word with a similar meaning, near a new word
  in a reading passage.

★ Look for an antonym, a word with an opposite meaning, near a new word
  in a reading passage.

★ Once you think you know the meaning of a new word, read the sentence where
  the word appears, using this new meaning. Does the sentence still make sense
  in the story? If so, you've probably figured out the meaning of the new word.

Read this article about swans. Then answer the questions.

> *Beautiful* and *serene* are two words that come to mind when a peaceful pair of snow-white swans glide across a still pond.
>
> "Absolutely wrong!" say some scientists. According to these experts, some swans are mean and nasty, especially mute swans. Mute swans are large birds. When they move into an area, they drive away smaller birds. They sometimes attack animals and people. Mute swans are also destructive. They cause damage to many kinds of plants. Mute swans eat four to eight pounds of plants a day. They even eat the roots. Many plants die and never grow back.
>
> The number of mute swans in parts of the United States is exploding! In Massachusetts alone, there are twice as many mute swans now as there were ten years ago. This would be okay if the birds that looked so delightful weren't so unpleasant.
>
> Officials in Rhode Island are desperate for help. Scientists there shake the nests of mute swans to keep the eggs from hatching. But they better watch out! Mute swans with eggs are even meaner!

5. In paragraph one, which clue word
   is a synonym of *serene?*
   Ⓐ beautiful   Ⓒ pond
   Ⓑ peaceful   Ⓓ snow-white

6. The word *unpleasant* is in paragraph
   three. Which clue word is an antonym
   of *unpleasant?*
   Ⓐ exploding   Ⓒ mute
   Ⓑ desperate   Ⓓ delightful

7. In paragraph two, which word gives
   a clue to the meaning of *destructive?*
   Ⓐ damage   Ⓒ plants
   Ⓑ people   Ⓓ roots

8. The best meaning of the word
   desperate in the last paragraph is
   Ⓐ "full of hope."
   Ⓑ "in great need."
   Ⓒ "dangerous or serious."
   Ⓓ "willing to give up."

Read this story about two friends who find an unexpected surprise while walking. Then answer the questions.

A Cry in the Woods

Ada stopped along the side of the wooded path. "Did you hear that?" Ada asked her friend Hasan. "I think I heard something. I think it might be a voice."

Hasan strained his ears. A faint cry of "help" seemed to echo in the woods. "I hear it too!" exclaimed Hasan.

"Follow me," Ada said as she burst down the path. "There's a clearing up ahead. We'll be able to see what's going on from there." Hasan hurried to stay close behind.

Together, the two friends followed the sound. When they arrived at the field, their eyes grew large and their tired legs came to a sudden stop.

There, in the clearing, were three small children, whimpering. They seemed tired and afraid. "We better help them," Ada said as she marched across the clearing. "They look as if they have been lost for hours."

9. In paragraph two, you can tell that the word *faint* means
   Ⓐ "fearful."
   Ⓑ "loud."
   Ⓒ "easy to find."
   Ⓓ "hard to hear."

10. In paragraph three, which word gives a clue to the meaning of *burst*?
   Ⓐ path
   Ⓑ clearing
   Ⓒ hurried
   Ⓓ behind

11. Which clue word is a synonym of *clearing*?
   Ⓐ path
   Ⓑ field
   Ⓒ sound
   Ⓓ cry

12. In the last paragraph, the best meaning of the word *whimpering* is
   Ⓐ "yelling loudly."
   Ⓑ "shaking with fear."
   Ⓒ "crying softly."
   Ⓓ "jumping happily."

★ A test question about finding meaning in context asks you about the meaning of a word as it is used in a reading passage. Some words have more than one meaning. Be sure you choose the correct meaning for the way the word is used in the passage.

★ A test question about finding meaning in context usually has several answer choices. Try each answer choice in the sentence in which the word appears. Decide which answer choice makes the most sense in the reading passage.

Here are the words to a song written by a cowboy.
Read the words to the song. Then do Numbers 13 and 14.

Red River Valley

From this valley they say you are going;
We will miss your bright eyes and sweet smile,
For they say you are taking the sunshine
That has brightened our pathway awhile.

Come and sit by my side if you love me.
Do not hasten to bid me **adieu**,
But remember the Red River Valley
And the cowboy that loves you so true.

adieu: a French word meaning "good-bye"

Won't you think of this valley you're leaving?
Oh, how lonely, how sad it will be.
Oh, think of the fond heart you're breaking
And the grief you are causing me.

Finding Word Meaning in Context

13. In the second verse, the word
hasten means
Ⓐ "come back again."
Ⓑ "stop suddenly."
Ⓒ "act quickly."
Ⓓ "whisper."

Finding Word Meaning in Context

14. In the last line, what is the best
meaning of the word *grief*?
Ⓐ "love"
Ⓑ "sadness"
Ⓒ "peace"
Ⓓ "happiness"

Here is an article written by a student for a school newspaper.
Read the article. Then do Numbers 15 and 16.

Students Need More Recess
by Carla Gonzalez

How many of you noticed that recess was cut by ten minutes this year? Last year, recess lasted twenty minutes. But this year, recess is only half that time.

Why the change? Well, I posed the question to our principal, Ms. Bates, last week.

"A new law was passed over the summer," explained Ms. Bates. "The law states that students need to spend more time learning in the classroom. As a result, the amount of time for daily recess had to be decreased."

So what can students do about this? Talk to your parents. Explain to them how important it is for us to have a longer recess. Students need to talk, run, and have fun. Recess helps us stay fit. Recess also helps us pay better attention during class. Ask them to help schools solve the time problem. Maybe then, we can get the twenty minutes of recess we need!

Finding Word Meaning in Context

15. In paragraph two, the word *posed* means
    Ⓐ "requested."
    Ⓑ "modeled."
    Ⓒ "presented."
    Ⓓ "answered."

Finding Word Meaning in Context

16. In paragraph three, the meaning of the word *decreased* is
    Ⓐ "made less or smaller."
    Ⓑ "done away with."
    Ⓒ "changed again."
    Ⓓ "found inside."

PART ONE: LEARN ABOUT DRAWING CONCLUSIONS AND MAKING INFERENCES

Read this story about a girl named Ana, who is at a gymnastics meet. As you read, try to figure out why the crowd is cheering at the end of the story.

Today was the day of the big gymnastics meet. It was Ana's turn on the balance beam. For months, Ana had been practicing her routine. She knew she had it down. But practice was one thing, and the meet was something else. There were hundreds of people here! She spotted her family sitting in the stands. They gave her an encouraging wave.

Ana got on the beam. Everything was going so well—her split, her forward roll, and her cartwheel. Now for the back flip! Ana could hear the crowd cheer. Those hours of practice had been worth it.

This story does not tell you why the crowd was cheering. It does, however, give you details that help you figure out why this happened.

Everything was going so well.
Those hours of practice had been worth it.

These details help you figure out that Ana's back flip was successful. Her routine started well. When she was done, she felt that the practice had been worth it. You probably know from your own experiences that by practicing something, you learn to do it better. You probably also know that people cheer when something good happens.

Details are sometimes not clearly explained in a reading passage. You must figure out some information on your own. Whenever you figure out something that is not told in a reading passage, you are **drawing a conclusion** or **making an inference**.

★ Pay attention to the details in a reading passage. You can use these details to figure out information that is not clearly stated.

★ Use the details from the reading passage and what you know from your own life to draw a conclusion or to make an inference.

Read this story about Davis, who has a problem with his favorite shirt. As you read, look for details that will help you figure out how Davis solved his problem. Then answer the questions.

Davis had a favorite shirt, a blue denim cowboy shirt. The shirt had five buttons shaped like cowboy boots.

One day Davis said, "Oh no! I lost a button. My favorite shirt is ruined!"

"Your shirt isn't ruined," said Mom. "I'll get Grandma's button box. You can find another button."

Davis wasn't happy. He knew Grandma's button box wouldn't have a button shaped like a cowboy boot. But he looked in the button box anyway.

There were shiny gold buttons. There were sparkling jewel-like buttons. Davis found a bumpy wooden button and a white glass button with red dots. There was even a button shaped like a star.

"Did you find another button for your shirt, Davis?" asked Mom.

"I sure did," said Davis. "Will you teach me how to sew buttons?"

"Of course," said Mom.

Now Davis has a favorite shirt—a blue denim cowboy shirt with twenty-five buttons!

1. From the story, you can tell that Davis solved his problem by
   Ⓐ buying himself a new cowboy shirt.
   Ⓑ sewing all the buttons he liked onto his favorite shirt.
   Ⓒ making a new shirt that was like his favorite one.
   Ⓓ looking for his lost button.

2. Which detail from the story helped you answer question 1?
   Ⓐ The shirt has five buttons shaped like cowboy boots.
   Ⓑ There were shiny gold buttons.
   Ⓒ There were sparkling jewel-like buttons.
   Ⓓ Now Davis has a favorite shirt— a blue-denim cowboy shirt with 25 buttons!

 Work with a partner. Talk about your answers to questions 1 and 2. Tell why you chose the answers you did.

Remember: Drawing a conclusion or making an inference is a way of figuring out information that is not stated in a reading passage.

★ Think about the details that are stated in a reading passage. Use these details to help you figure out information that is not explained.

★ Use the details from the reading passage and what you know from your own life to draw a conclusion or to make an inference.

Read this fable about a crow. As you read, ask yourself, "What details are explained? What information can I figure out on my own?" Then answer the questions.

There once was a crow that thought he was treated very unfairly. Every day, he watched while the farmer threw out food for the doves to eat. The crow, on the other hand, had to scratch and search for every bite of food. "This isn't fair," thought the crow. He decided to do something about it.

The crow covered himself with white powder. Then he quietly entered the dovecote. The doves thought the crow was one of them. They greeted him and shared their food with him. "This is the life!" thought the crow. Everything went smoothly until one day when the crow spoke, and let out a very crowlike, "Caw! Caw! Caw!" The doves realized at once that this new bird was a crow and not a dove. They chased him out of the dovecote.

The crow tried to return to live with the other crows. But the crows did not recognize this white bird. They would have nothing to do with him.

3. You can tell that the crow covered himself with white powder so that he
   Ⓐ could trick the farmer.
   Ⓑ would look like a dove.
   Ⓒ would be liked by other crows.
   Ⓓ could steal food from other birds.

4. You can tell from this fable that
   Ⓐ crows look very much like doves, except for their color.
   Ⓑ doves and crows make the same sounds.
   Ⓒ doves do not like to share their food.
   Ⓓ crows never have enough food to eat.

Look at the answer choices for each question. Read why each answer choice is correct or not correct.

3. You can tell that the crow covered himself with white powder so that he

   Ⓐ could trick the farmer.

   This answer is not correct because the details in the fable show that the crow was trying to trick the other doves, not the farmer.

   ● would look like a dove.

   This answer is correct because after the crow covered himself with white powder, he went to the dovecote. You can figure out from this detail that the crow must have thought that covering himself with white powder would make him look like a dove.

   Ⓒ would be liked by other crows.

   This answer is not correct because there are no details that tell about the crow not being liked by other crows. At the end of the fable, the crows will have nothing to do with him only because they did not recognize him.

   Ⓓ could steal food from other birds.

   This answer is not correct because there are no details that tell that the crow wanted to steal in order to get the food he needed.

4. You can tell from this fable that

   ● crows look very much like doves, except for their color.

   This answer is correct because after the crow covered himself with white powder, the doves thought that he was a dove. You can figure out that crows and doves must look very much alike, except for their color.

   Ⓑ doves and crows make the same sounds.

   This answer is not correct because the details in the fable tell you that once the crow spoke and made a crowlike sound, the doves knew he wasn't one of them. You can figure out from this detail that doves and crows do not make the same sounds.

   Ⓒ doves do not like to share their food.

   This answer is not correct because the details explain that doves do share their food, but only with other doves.

   Ⓓ crows never have enough food to eat.

   This answer is not correct because the details tell about only one crow who is upset that the farmer never puts out food for him.

★ Look for details in a reading passage that tell about the way a person or character looks, acts, thinks, feels, and speaks. Think about how people with similar qualities act.

★ Think about where something happens or when it happens in a reading passage. If something happens near the Statue of Liberty, you can figure out that the setting is New York. If something happens as the sun is rising, you can figure out that it is morning.

Read this article about an American boy who visits his family in India. Then answer the questions.

> Hiren Patel grew up in the United States. But his ancestors are from Gujarat, India. A few months ago, Hiren visited his cousins there.
>
> "In India, we eat with our hands," Hiren says. After dinner, Hiren washes his hands in the sink. The sinks are right next to the dinner table.
>
> "Sometimes, we sit on the floor with our legs crossed Indian style," Hiren says. Everyone serves himself or herself, taking a little from each dish.
>
> To Hindu Indians, like Hiren, the cow is sacred. That means he can't eat meat. "The cow gives us milk and helps us with our land," says Hiren. "Why would we hurt something that helps in so many ways?" Hiren also eats only with his right hand. And he doesn't eat fish. But he does eat chicken and eggs.
>
> "Pizza Hut just opened near my cousin's house," Hiren reports. "None of the pizza served there has meat on it."

5. You can tell from the article that Hiren
   Ⓐ doesn't care about what he eats.
   Ⓑ eats only certain foods.
   Ⓒ eats whatever foods he wants.
   Ⓓ doesn't enjoy eating pizza.

6. You can tell that a good meal to serve Hiren if he came to your house for dinner is
   Ⓐ hamburgers and French fries.
   Ⓑ spaghetti and meatballs.
   Ⓒ steak and mashed potatoes.
   Ⓓ chicken and rice.

7. From the article, you can tell that Hiren
   Ⓐ was born in India.
   Ⓑ lives with his cousin.
   Ⓒ lives in India.
   Ⓓ has family in India.

8. The pizza restaurant near Hiren's cousin's house probably doesn't serve meat pizza because
   Ⓐ most of the customer's don't like the taste of meat.
   Ⓑ there is no meat available in India.
   Ⓒ most of the customer's don't eat meat.
   Ⓓ meat is too expensive to buy in India.

Read this article about the country of Japan. Then answer the questions.

Japan is an island country in Asia. Japan is made up of four large islands and over 3,000 smaller ones. The main islands are Hokkaido, Honshu, Kyushu, and Shikoku.

Japan is a small country with a large population. Mountains cover much of Japan. This land cannot be developed for homes. It is also not good for farming. Most people live close together in cities near the ocean. This makes some areas of Japan very crowded.

Japan has many interesting and unique features. Mount Fuji is the highest point in Japan. It is a volcano that has not erupted in 250 years. The Kanto Plain is the largest area of flat land in Japan. This plain is home to Japan's capital city, Tokyo.

The first people settled in Japan more than 8,000 years ago. Over time, they came to call their country Nippon. This name means "Land of the Rising Sun." Nippon is the name that is still used in Japan today.

9. From the article, you can tell that Japan has
   Ⓐ few cities.
   Ⓑ few farms.
   Ⓒ few people.
   Ⓓ few islands.

10. Details in the article suggest that Japan is
    Ⓐ larger than the United States.
    Ⓑ made up of many plains.
    Ⓒ surrounded by water.
    Ⓓ home to the largest plain in the world.

11. What can you conclude about Mt. Fuji from the article?
    Ⓐ It is located in Tokyo.
    Ⓑ It is an active volcano.
    Ⓒ It is the highest mountain in the world.
    Ⓓ It is not an active volcano.

12. Which of these would you probably not find in Japan?
    Ⓐ large numbers of people
    Ⓑ tall office buildings
    Ⓒ large areas of flat land
    Ⓓ busy ocean cities

★ A test question about drawing conclusions or making inferences asks you to figure out something that is not stated in a reading passage.

★ A test question about drawing conclusions or making inferences often contains the words *you can tell, determine,* or *conclude.*

Here is a story about an unusual event. Read the story.
Then do Numbers 13 and 14.

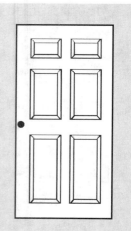

"I'd be careful if I were you," a soft voice called as Sara prepared to open the closet door.

Sara turned around, expecting to see who was talking. But there was no one in the room. There was only a tall grandfather clock, a few pieces of furniture, and a large window that filled the room with a hint of moonlight. "Who said that?" Sara asked, confused.

"I did," said the clock.

Sara's eyes widened. She approached the clock and said, "You? *You* spoke to me?"

"I think I must tell you about the door you almost opened. See that sign on the door that says OPEN CAREFULLY? There is a reason for that sign. That door is no ordinary door. If you open it, your life will be changed forever. So, remember—open it *carefully.*"

"Thanks for the warning," Sara said as she placed her hand on the doorknob. She paused for a moment and then removed her hand. After a few minutes, she reached for the doorknob again. Slowly, Sara opened the door. Almost immediately, a brilliant light poured into the room. Within seconds, Sara arrived in a strange and magical world.

Drawing Conclusions and
Making Inferences

13. You can tell that the story takes place
    Ⓐ long ago.
    Ⓑ at night.
    Ⓒ in a castle.
    Ⓓ at dawn.

Drawing Conclusions and
Making Inferences

14. You can tell that Sara
    Ⓐ was afraid of the talking clock.
    Ⓑ wished she had not opened the door.
    Ⓒ almost changed her mind about opening the door.
    Ⓓ did not see the sign on the door.

Here is a folktale from Africa. Read the folktale. Then do Numbers 15 and 16.

Some time ago, a baby snake set out to play. As he slithered away, his mother spoke this rhyme: "Watch out young son, for things with claws, for things with a beak, for things with strong jaws."

"Claws, beak, jaws. Claws, beak, jaws," Snake Baby repeated.

At the same time, a baby frog set out to play. As he hopped away, his mother spoke this rhyme: "Watch out for the hiss, watch out for the coil, watch out for the squeeze, they will cause turmoil."

"Hiss, coil, squeeze. Hiss, coil, squeeze," Frog Baby repeated.

Snake Baby and Frog Baby met in the rain forest and played games all day. First they played leap frog. Then they played hide and hug.

That night, Frog Baby told his mother about the games he played.

"No, no, Frog Baby! Hide and hug is not a game for you. It is the game of the hiss, coil, and squeeze. Promise you will never play with him again."

Snake Baby also told his mother about the games he played.

"No, no, Snake Baby! Hide and hug is not a game for you. Hide and hug is what you must do. This is the way you get your meals! Promise me you will hiss, coil, and squeeze."

Drawing Conclusions and Making Inferences

15. From the folktale, you can tell that
    Ⓐ Snake Baby will eat Frog Baby.
    Ⓑ Snake Baby will never hiss, coil, or squeeze again.
    Ⓒ Frog Baby will still play safely with Snake Baby.
    Ⓓ Frog Baby will be in danger if he plays with Snake Baby again.

Drawing Conclusions and Making Inferences

16. From the folktale, you can tell that
    Ⓐ frogs are smarter than snakes.
    Ⓑ frogs are a danger to snakes.
    Ⓒ snakes are supposed to eat frogs.
    Ⓓ snakes are afraid of frogs.

PART ONE: LEARN ABOUT DISTINGUISHING BETWEEN FACT AND OPINION

Read this paragraph about San Francisco. As you read, look for statements that can be proved. Also look for statements that tell what someone thinks or feels.

San Francisco is located in California. I believe this city is the most beautiful city in the United States. The blue waters of the Pacific Ocean lie to the west. San Francisco Bay is to the east. The Golden Gate Bridge connects the city to northern California. San Francisco is the perfect spot for your next vacation!

The statements that can be proved are

San Francisco is located in California.
The blue waters of the Pacific Ocean lie to the west.
San Francisco Bay is to the east.
The Golden Gate Bridge connects the city to northern California.

The statements that tell what someone thinks or feels are

I believe this city is the most beautiful city in the United States.
San Francisco is the perfect spot for your next vacation!

If a statement can be proved, it is a **fact**. If a statement tells what someone thinks or feels about something, it is an **opinion**. Facts can be proved. Opinions cannot. When you figure out if a statement is a fact or an opinion, you are **distinguishing between fact and opinion**.

★ Facts are statements that can be checked or proved.

★ Opinions are statements that cannot be proved. They tell what someone thinks or feels.

★ Opinions often contain such clue words as *think, feel, believe,* and *seem.* Other common clue words are *always, never, all, none, most, least, greatest, best,* and *worst.*

Read this movie review written by a ten-year-old boy. As you read, ask yourself, "Which statements can be proved? Which statements cannot be proved?" Then answer the questions.

Badzilla

If you like scary movies, I think you will love the new movie *Badzilla*. If you don't like scary movies, stay home. *Badzilla* is not the movie for you. There has never been a movie ever made that is scarier than *Badzilla*.

Badzilla is the name of the monster in the movie. Badzilla is half-robot and half-human. He was made by a scientist named Dr. Norma Tate. One day, *Badzilla* escapes from the lab where he was built. Dr. Tate sets off on a trip across the country to save her greatest creation.

Badzilla is now showing at Global Theater. It is also showing at Reed's Cinema downtown. If you can, see the movie at Global Theater. It's the best theater in town.

1. Which of these is a fact?
   Ⓐ *Badzilla* is not the movie for you.
   Ⓑ *Badzilla* is now showing at Global Theater.
   Ⓒ There has never been a movie ever made that is scarier than *Badzilla*.
   Ⓓ If you like scary movies, I think you will love the new movie *Badzilla*.

2. Which clue word signals an opinion about Global Theater?
   Ⓐ greatest
   Ⓑ think
   Ⓒ never
   Ⓓ best

 Work with a partner. Talk about your answers to questions 1 and 2. Tell why you chose the answers you did.

Remember: Facts can be proved, but opinions cannot be proved.

★ To find out if a statement is a fact, ask yourself, "Can this statement be proved?"

★ To find out if a statement is an opinion, ask yourself, "Does this statement tell what someone thinks or feels?"

★ Look for clue words that signal an opinion, such as *think, feel, believe, seem, always, never, all, none, most, least, greatest, best,* and *worst.*

Read this story about a boy who lives in Ghana. As you read, think about which statements are facts and which statements are opinions. Then answer the questions.

My name is Asare, and I am from Ghana. I think you do not know very much about Ghana, so I will tell you a little bit.

Ghana is a country on the west coast of Africa. I live with my family near the capital of Accra. My father is a fisherman. He says that fishing has changed a lot in the past years. When my great-grandfather was a fisherman, he carved his own boat out of wood. He sailed out to sea with many other men, each in his own canoe. Today, my father still fishes from a canoe. But his canoe has a motor. It is much better to have a boat with a motor.

In Ghana, many people fish in Lake Volta. Lake Volta is a very large lake in the eastern part of Ghana. But my father fishes in the Atlantic Ocean. When he catches tuna, I am the happiest boy in Ghana. Tuna is the most delicious fish!

3. Which of these statements tells what someone thinks or feels?
   Ⓐ My name is Asare, and I am from Ghana.
   Ⓑ In Ghana, many people fish in Lake Volta.
   Ⓒ But my father fishes in the Atlantic Ocean.
   Ⓓ Tuna is the most delicious fish!

4. Which of these statements can be proved?
   Ⓐ I am the happiest boy in Ghana.
   Ⓑ It is much better to have a boat with a motor.
   Ⓒ Lake Volta is a very large lake in the eastern part of Ghana.
   Ⓓ I think you do not know very much about Ghana.

Look at the answer choices for each question. Read why each answer choice is correct or not correct.

3. Which of these statements tells what someone thinks or feels?

Ⓐ My name is Asare, and I am from Ghana.

This answer is not correct because this statement is a fact. It can be proved that this is the boy's name.

Ⓑ In Ghana, many people fish in Lake Volta.

This answer is not correct because this statement is a fact. It can be proved, by watching or observing the lake, that many people fish there.

Ⓒ But my father fishes in the Atlantic Ocean.

This answer is not correct because this statement is a fact. It can be proved, by watching or observing Asare's father, that his father fishes in the Atlantic Ocean.

● Tuna is the most delicious fish!

This answer is correct because it tells how Asare feels about the taste of tuna. This statement cannot be proved.

4. Which of these statements can be proved?

Ⓐ I am the happiest boy in Ghana.

This answer is not correct because it cannot be proved that Asare is the happiest boy in Ghana. Most likely, other boys are as happy, or happier, than he at certain times.

Ⓑ It is much better to have a boat with a motor.

This answer is not correct because it cannot be proved. This statement tells how Asare feels about which kind of boat is better. Most likely, other people have different ideas about what kind of boat is better. The clue word better signals that this statement is an opinion, not a fact.

● Lake Volta is a very large lake in the eastern part of Ghana.

This answer is correct because it can be proved. You can find facts about Lake Volta in an encyclopedia or atlas.

Ⓓ I think you do not know very much about Ghana.

This answer is not correct because it cannot be proved. Asare has no idea how much the readers of his story know about Ghana. The clue word think signals that this statement is an opinion, not a fact.

★ Facts can be checked or tested. You can prove that a fact is correct or true.

★ Opinions express someone's thoughts, feelings, or beliefs. An opinion can be about an event, an idea, a person, or a thing. Even if a person agrees or disagrees with an opinion, it still cannot be proved.

Read this article written by a student about wind. Then answer the questions.

Wind is the most amazing force. Wind is something that you can't see, but you know when it is there. You can feel it. I love the feeling of wind blowing through my hair.

Wind is air that is moving. Sometimes, the air moves slowly, and there is a gentle breeze. Wind can also move quickly, causing strong winds. A strong wind can knock down a tree or a power line. The best wind is a gentle wind.

Besides speed, wind has direction. Winds are described by the direction from which they come. A north wind blows from the north to the south. A south wind blows from the south to the north.

Though you can't see wind, you can see its effects. Trees sway, windows rattle, and leaves are blown from their branches. There is nothing more fun than watching fall leaves whirling around like a tornado.

5. Which of these is a fact from the article?
   Ⓐ Wind is air that is moving.
   Ⓑ The best wind is a gentle wind.
   Ⓒ The wind is the most amazing force.
   Ⓓ There is nothing more fun than watching fall leaves whirling around like a tornado.

6. Which of these statements tells what someone thinks or feels?
   Ⓐ A strong wind can knock down a tree.
   Ⓑ Besides speed, wind has direction.
   Ⓒ I love the feeling of wind blowing through my hair.
   Ⓓ A south wind blows from the south to the north.

7. Which of these clue words signals an opinion about a gentle wind?
   Ⓐ most
   Ⓑ best
   Ⓒ always
   Ⓓ feel

8. Which is a fact about wind that can be proved?
   Ⓐ Wind is the most amazing force.
   Ⓑ The best wind is a gentle wind.
   Ⓒ Wind is something you can't see.
   Ⓓ There is nothing more fun than watching fall leaves whirling around like a tornado.

Look at the answer choices for each question. Read why each answer choice is correct or not correct.

3. The author wrote the passage mainly to

● entertain readers with a story about his pencil collection.

This answer is correct because the passage mainly tells a personal story that is enjoyable to read.

Ⓑ explain how to start a coin collection.

This answer is not correct because the passage does not contain information that explains how to start a coin collection. The author mentions only that some people collect coins, not how to start a coin collection.

Ⓒ make readers believe that pencil collections are better than other collections.

This answer is not correct because the passage does not contain opinions about one kind of collection being better than another kind of collection.

Ⓓ describe the kind of pencils that he collects.

This answer is not correct because the passage does not mainly provide lots of details about the kinds of pencils the author collects.

4. You know your answer to question 3 is correct because the passage mainly

Ⓐ contains many details that describe something.

This answer is not correct because the passage does not contain lots of details that describe a particular person, place, or thing. The passage does provide some descriptions about the pencils in the author's collection, but this is not the main purpose of the passage.

Ⓑ provides facts or tells readers how to do something.

This answer is not correct because the passage does not mainly contain facts or information that teaches or explains how to do something.

Ⓒ tries to convince readers of something.

This answer is not correct because the passage does not mainly contain opinions that try to get readers to do, buy, or believe something.

● tells an enjoyable story.

This answer is correct because the passage tells a personal story about something the author finds fun to do.

Different reading passages are written for different purposes. Knowing the kind of passage you are reading often helps you identify the author's purpose.

★ Articles are usually written to describe or explain. Some articles describe a person, place, or thing. Others explain something, such as the cause of pollution or the meaning of friendship.

★ Directions are written to explain.

★ Personal stories, riddles, and poetry are written to entertain.

★ Ads and articles in which an opinion is stated are written to persuade.

Read each passage. Then answer the questions.

**I   The Bird House
28 Main St., Groton**

We have the largest selection of birdseed, birdbaths, and feeders in town. We also have the lowest prices! You won't find a better deal anywhere! Come see us today!

II   My Window

I have a birdfeeder on the outside of my window. If I stay really still, I can watch the birds as they eat. One day, a little bird was trying to eat, but a bigger bird kept chasing him away. I was worried about the little bird. So I got an idea. I put a picture of my cat on the window. The next time the big bird came by, he flew away. And he's never come back!

III   Easy Birdfeeder

First, find a large pinecone. Then fill all the open spaces with peanut butter. Next, roll the pinecone in birdseed. Add a string to hang your birdfeeder from a tree. Now sit back and wait for the birds to arrive!

IV   The Cardinal

The cardinal is a bird that is enjoyed by many bird-watchers. The cardinal is found in the eastern United States. It is also found in parts of Mexico and California. The male is bright red with a black throat. The female is mostly brown, with red on its wings and tail. Both birds have a red cluster of feathers on their head.

---

5. The author's main purpose in passage I is to
   Ⓐ describe.   Ⓒ entertain.
   Ⓑ explain.   Ⓓ persuade.

6. The author's main purpose in passage II is to
   Ⓐ describe.   Ⓒ entertain.
   Ⓑ explain.   Ⓓ persuade.

7. The author's main purpose in passage III is to
   Ⓐ describe.   Ⓒ entertain.
   Ⓑ explain.   Ⓓ persuade.

8. The author's main purpose in passage IV is to
   Ⓐ describe.   Ⓒ entertain.
   Ⓑ explain.   Ⓓ persuade.

Read this fable about two frogs. Then answer the questions.

The Frogs and the Well

There were once two frogs that lived together in a marsh. The marsh was a wonderful place for frogs. There were always lots of bugs to eat and lots of water for playing and drinking.

One hot summer day, the marsh dried up. Frogs like wet, damp places, and now the marsh was as dry as a desert. The two frogs decided to find a new place to live.

After a while, the two frogs came to a deep well. One of the frogs looked down into the well and saw water. He said to his friend, "This looks like a nice, cool place. Let us jump in and settle here."

The other frog had a much wiser head on his shoulders. He replied, "Not so fast, my friend. What if the well dries up one day? How could we possibly get out of the well?"

The moral of the fable: *Look before you leap.*

9. The author wrote paragraph one mainly to
   Ⓐ explain why the frogs lived in a marsh.
   Ⓑ try to get readers to learn about a marsh.
   Ⓒ describe the marsh where the frogs lived.
   Ⓓ entertain readers with a funny joke about a marsh.

10. The author wrote paragraph two mainly to
   Ⓐ entertain readers with a story about frogs.
   Ⓑ explain why the frogs had to move.
   Ⓒ describe how the marsh dried up.
   Ⓓ persuade readers to feel sorry for the frogs.

11. The author wrote paragraph three mainly to
   Ⓐ describe the place where one frog wanted to settle.
   Ⓑ explain why the frogs were looking for a new home.
   Ⓒ persuade readers to learn more about deep wells.
   Ⓓ entertain readers with a silly story about a frog.

12. The author wrote the fable mainly to
   Ⓐ explain why frogs don't live in wells.
   Ⓑ persuade readers to avoid wells.
   Ⓒ entertain readers with a story that teaches a lesson.
   Ⓓ describe what a well looks like.

★ A test question about identifying the author's purpose may ask you why an author probably wrote a particular reading passage. This kind of question is asking about the purpose of the entire reading passage.

★ A test question about identifying the author's purpose may ask you why a particular paragraph was written. This kind of question is asking about only one part of the reading passage.

**Here are instructions for making something for your room.
Read the instructions. Then do Numbers 13 and 14.**

In some foreign countries, rooms are not separated by doors. Rooms are separated by a curtain made of hanging strands of beads. When a person walks through the beads, a wonderful clicking sound fills the air. You can make a similar curtain out of drinking straws. It won't be pleasantly noisy, but it is fun to make.

Things you need
- drinking straws
- string
- scissors
- cord
- heavy-duty tape
- beads or small tube macaroni

1. Cut drinking straws into small pieces to make beads. (a)
2. Cut lengths of string as long as you want your curtain to be.
3. Tie one end of a length of string to a bead or tube macaroni. (b)
4. Add pieces of straw to the string, until you have covered up most of the string. (c)
5. Cut a length of cord as wide as you wish the curtain to be. (d)
6. Tie the string of straws to one end of the cord. (e)
7. Make more strings of straws and tie them to the cord.
8. Have an adult help you hang the curtain inside a doorway with heavy-duty tape.

Identifying Author's Purpose

13. The author wrote the first paragraph mainly to
    Ⓐ persuade readers to make a curtain.
    Ⓑ describe a kind of curtain used in some foreign countries.
    Ⓒ explain how to make a curtain.
    Ⓓ entertain readers with a funny story.

Identifying Author's Purpose

14. The instructions were written mainly to
    Ⓐ explain how to make something.
    Ⓑ describe something about foreign countries.
    Ⓒ get readers to make a curtain for their room.
    Ⓓ entertain readers with an article about straws.

Here is an article about a unique invention. Read the article.
Then do Numbers 15 and 16.

In the early 1940s, James Wright created a new type of rubber for a company named General Electric. His invention could bounce higher than a rubber ball and could lift ink off a newspaper page. However, this new rubber did not have any practical uses for General Electric. The company mailed samples of the new rubber to several people to see if they could find a good use for it.

Some time later, a toy-store worker named Paul Hodgson saw a group of adults playing with this rubber. He was surprised at how much fun they were having. Hodgson wrote to General Electric and asked if he could sell the rubber. In 1949, he began to sell the rubber in packages shaped like eggs. Hodgson called it Silly Putty. Silly Putty became a huge success. At long last, a use for the new rubber had been found.

Identifying Author's Purpose

15. The author wrote the first paragraph mainly to
    Ⓐ describe a new kind of rubber that was invented.
    Ⓑ explain how rubber is made.
    Ⓒ try to get readers to try out their own inventions.
    Ⓓ entertain readers with a story about silly inventions.

Identifying Author's Purpose

16. The article was written mainly to
    Ⓐ persuade readers to buy Silly Putty.
    Ⓑ describe how Silly Putty works.
    Ⓒ explain how a popular toy was invented.
    Ⓓ entertain readers with a story about Silly Putty.

PART ONE: LEARN ABOUT INTERPRETING FIGURATIVE LANGUAGE

Read this sentence. As you read, think about the two things being compared.

> ### The tornado was as fierce as a *T. Rex.*
> The two things being compared are a tornado and a *T. Rex.*
> The writer used a **simile** to help readers picture how terrible the tornado was.
> A simile uses the word *like* or *as* to compare two things.

Read this sentence. As you read, think about the two things being compared.

> ### Ned's legs were shaking leaves.
> The two things being compared are Ned's legs and shaking leaves.
> The writer used a **metaphor** to help readers picture how nervous Ned was.
> A metaphor compares two things but does not use the word *like* or *as.*
> A metaphor says that one thing is another thing.

Now read this sentence. As you read, think about the meaning of the underlined words.

> ### The dog <u>turned up her nose</u> at the food.
> The underlined words mean that the dog did not care for the food.
> The underlined words are an **idiom.**
> An idiom is a phrase whose words have a meaning different from their usual meaning.

Similes, metaphors, and idioms are types of figurative language. Authors use figurative language to help readers create pictures in their mind. When you understand the meaning of a simile, a metaphor, or an idiom, you are **interpreting figurative language**.

★ Look for things that are compared in a reading passage. Try to find examples of similes or metaphors.

★ Look for phrases whose words have a meaning different from their usual meaning. Try to find examples of idioms.

★ Figurative language usually brings a picture to a reader's mind. Use that picture to help you understand the meaning of the figurative language.

Read this article about the athlete Mia Hamm. As you read, look for things that are compared. Also look for words that have a meaning different from their usual meaning. Then answer the questions.

Many soccer fans believe that Mia Hamm is the best female soccer player in the world. She has the speed of a cheetah. She can also stop and change direction as quick as a fox. These are important skills for a soccer player.

Mia played on the United States Olympic soccer team in 1996. The U.S. women's team beat China to win a gold medal. For Mia, it was a victory for all female athletes.

What does a new sports star do after winning a gold medal? Mia and her sister visited New York City for a little fun. They said they were going to have a ball.

1. In the article, Mia's speed is compared to the speed of
   Ⓐ a sports star.
   Ⓑ a fox.
   Ⓒ a soccer player.
   Ⓓ a cheetah.

2. In the last paragraph, what do the words *have a ball* mean?
   Ⓐ play soccer
   Ⓑ enjoy themselves
   Ⓒ take a tour
   Ⓓ act foolishly

 Work with a partner. Talk about your answers to questions 1 and 2. Tell why you chose the answers you did.

Remember: Similes, metaphors, and idioms are types of figurative language. Authors use figurative language to help readers create pictures in their mind.

★ Look for things that are compared in a reading passage.

★ Look for phrases whose words have a meaning different from their usual meaning.

★ Think about any pictures that come to mind as you read. Use those pictures to help you understand what is being described.

Read this article about a famous painting. As you read, ask yourself, "What pictures come to mind?" Then answer the questions.

Have you seen this painting before? This is a famous painting by the American artist Grant Wood. The painting is called *American Gothic.*

Grant Wood painted *American Gothic* in 1930. The painting was an overnight success. Wood was glad that so many people enjoyed his painting. He wanted everyday people, not just other artists, to enjoy his paintings.

Most people liked the way the man and woman in the painting looked. They appeared to be serious and hardworking. Many people thought that the couple looked the way all Americans should look. Others thought the couple looked as stiff as a tree trunk.

Today, we see copies of Wood's painting in cartoons and advertisements. Sometimes, the faces of the man and woman are changed. They are replaced with the faces of famous people, like movie stars or other people in the news. Sometimes, the man and woman are put in a new setting. Keep your eye out for these two. You never know where they might turn up.

3. In paragraph two, the words *overnight success* mean
   - Ⓐ "liked by only a few people."
   - Ⓑ "viewed at night."
   - Ⓒ "became popular right away."
   - Ⓓ "took a long time to become known."

4. In paragraph three, the couple in the painting is compared to a
   - Ⓐ cartoon.
   - Ⓑ movie star.
   - Ⓒ painting.
   - Ⓓ tree trunk.

INTERPRETING FIGURATIVE LANGUAGE

Look at the answer choices for each question. Read why each answer choice is correct or not correct.

3. In paragraph two, the words *overnight success* mean

Ⓐ "liked by only a few people."

This answer is not correct because there are no details in the article to hint that only a few people liked the painting. In fact, the article states, "Most people liked the way the man and woman in the painting looked."

Ⓑ "viewed at night."

This answer is not correct because there are no details in the article to hint that the painting was seen at night.

● "became popular right away."

This answer is correct because details in the article hint that the painting became liked by many people rather quickly. The article states, "Wood was glad that so many people enjoyed his painting."

Ⓓ "took a long time to become known."

This answer is not correct because there are no details in the article to hint that the painting took a long time to be known by others.

4. In paragraph three, the couple in the painting is compared to a

Ⓐ cartoon.

This answer is not correct because there is no comparison made between the couple and a cartoon. In paragraph four, the article states that the couple sometimes appears in cartoons, but this is not a comparison.

Ⓑ movie star.

This answer is not correct because there is no comparison made between the couple and a movie star. In paragraph four, the article states that the faces of the couple are sometimes replaced with the faces of movie stars, but this is not a comparison.

Ⓒ painting.

This answer is not correct because there is no comparison made between the couple and a painting. The article states that the couple appears in a famous painting, but this is not a comparison.

● tree trunk.

This answer is correct because in paragraph three, the article states, "Others thought the couple looked as stiff as a tree trunk." The word as *signals that two things are being compared in a simile.*

★ Think about the things being compared in a simile or a metaphor. Ask yourself, "What do the two things have in common?" This will help you create pictures in your mind.

★ Look at the sentences near an idiom. You might find context clues to help you figure out its meaning.

Read this tall tale about Paul Bunyan. Then answer the questions.

Paul Bunyan is the hero of many tall tales. There are more stories about Paul Bunyan than there are trees in a forest. Most of the stories tell about the amazing things that Paul did.

No one seems to know exactly when Paul was born. Most folks, however, agree that he was the biggest, strongest baby that anyone had ever seen. As a baby, he was already as large as a horse, and just as hungry. He wrestled bears for fun. But Paul's favorite playmate was a big blue ox named Babe.

Paul was a lumberjack. He became famous for chopping down the forests that once covered America. Working like busy beavers, Paul and Babe cleared the land for farms and settlers. After one day of very hard work, Paul and Babe were thirsty. So they dug themselves the Great Lakes so that they would always have plenty of water to drink.

After Paul and Babe had cleared enough land for the settlers' farms, they went to Canada. From there, they decided to head out for Alaska. Just where they are today, no one is quite sure.

5. In paragraph two, Paul's size is compared to that of
   Ⓐ an ox.   Ⓒ a horse.
   Ⓑ a tree.   Ⓓ a forest.

6. The sentence *There are more stories about Paul than there are trees in a forest* means that there are
   Ⓐ few stories about Paul.
   Ⓑ a lot of stories about Paul.
   Ⓒ stories about Paul that are hard to believe.
   Ⓓ stories about Paul that always take place in a forest.

7. The tall tale says that Paul and Babe worked like busy beavers. This means that they
   Ⓐ worked in ponds.
   Ⓑ worked slowly.
   Ⓒ worked like farmers.
   Ⓓ worked hard and long.

8. In the last paragraph, the phrase *head out* means
   Ⓐ "live in."
   Ⓑ "travel toward."
   Ⓒ "travel away from."
   Ⓓ "plan a trip."

Read this article about a World Cup soccer game. Then answer the questions.

In July 1998, France and Brazil faced each other for soccer's highest honor, the World Cup. The World Cup is to soccer what the World Series is to baseball.

Some people thought the French team didn't stand a chance against Brazil. Brazil was the better team, they said. Brazil had Ronaldo. Ronaldo has been called the world's best soccer player. Some have said that Ronaldo was a tiger on the field.

But France had Zinedine Ziane, the French magician. Ziane was an excellent player, but he did not often score goals. In the game against Brazil, Ziane scored two goals. "I was so hungry to score a World Cup goal that I made it two," he said. The final score was 3–0. France was the new world champion!

World Cup

9. In the article, the World Cup is compared to
   Ⓐ a soccer game.
   Ⓑ a high honor.
   Ⓒ a baseball game.
   Ⓓ the World Series.

10. Which two things are compared in paragraph three?
    Ⓐ a soccer game and a magic trick
    Ⓑ a champion and a country
    Ⓒ a soccer player and a magician
    Ⓓ a soccer team and a goal

11. The words *didn't stand a chance* mean that the French team
    Ⓐ was expected to win easily.
    Ⓑ probably wouldn't play well.
    Ⓒ didn't have much hope of winning.
    Ⓓ had few players who could score.

12. Which of these is a metaphor?
    Ⓐ Ronaldo was a tiger on the field.
    Ⓑ Brazil was the better team.
    Ⓒ Ziane scored two goals.
    Ⓓ I was so hungry to score a World Cup goal.

★ A test question about interpreting figurative language may ask you about the meaning of a simile, a metaphor, or an idiom.

★ A test question about interpreting figurative language may ask you about things that are compared in the reading passage.

Here is a story about a boy's visit to a museum. Read the story. Then do Numbers 13 and 14.

> Roberto had just entered the museum with his parents. This was his first trip to the museum, but he wasn't very happy. His friends from school told him that a visit to the museum was about as much fun as cleaning one's room.
>
> As Roberto walked in the museum, he saw old airplanes and space rockets. He saw an enormous skeleton of a brontosaurus towering high above a group of gathering children. Roberto even saw a woman showing a group of children how a light bulb works. Roberto quickly became excited. "My friends must be pulling my leg! Museums have all sorts of fun things," Roberto thought to himself. Roberto knew that his first trip to the museum certainly wouldn't be his last.

Interpreting Figurative Language

13. In the story, a visit to the museum is compared to
    Ⓐ going to school.
    Ⓑ looking at old airplanes.
    Ⓒ cleaning one's room.
    Ⓓ flying a rocket.

Interpreting Figurative Language

14. The words *pulling my leg* mean that Roberto thinks his friends are
    Ⓐ harming him.
    Ⓑ fooling him.
    Ⓒ helping him.
    Ⓓ pushing him.

Here is an article about the first space-shuttle mission. Read the article. Then do Numbers 15 and 16.

On April 2, 1981, the space shuttle *Columbia* lifted off from Cape Canaveral, Florida. Captain John Young and Commander Robert Crippen were chosen to pilot this first space-shuttle flight. Their mission was to prove that a shuttle could work in space, and that it could be used for more than one mission.

Scientists had never tested the shuttle in space before. They were nervous during the launch. Scientists watched like hawks as the *Columbia* left the ground.

Young and Crippen spent two days in space. In that time, they were able to prove what scientists had hoped for. When the mission was completed on April 14, *Columbia* landed safely in California. Scientists were excited to find that their years of hard work were about to pay off.

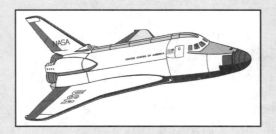

Interpreting Figurative Language

15. The words *watched liked hawks* mean that the scientists watched
   Ⓐ slowly.
   Ⓑ happily.
   Ⓒ carefully.
   Ⓓ while flying.

Interpreting Figurative Language

16. In the last sentence, the words *pay off* mean
   Ⓐ "bring success."
   Ⓑ "cause failure."
   Ⓒ "receive money."
   Ⓓ "cause injury."

PART ONE: LEARN ABOUT DISTINGUISHING BETWEEN REAL AND MAKE-BELIEVE

Read this story about an unusual dog. As you read, think about the things that could really happen and the things that could not really happen.

> Rusty had woken up when the first glimmer of sun appeared. He spent the day exploring the countryside. Rusty was ready to go home. He ran up to a yellow cab. The shaggy dog opened the door and jumped in. Rusty told the driver to take him home.

The things that could really happen
Rusty had woken up when the first glimmer of sun appeared.
He spent the day exploring the countryside.
Rusty was ready to go home.
He ran up to a yellow cab.

The things that could not really happen
The shaggy dog opened the door and jumped in.
Rusty told the driver to take him home.

Things you read that could happen in real life are **real.** Things you read that could not happen in real life are **make-believe.** When you figure out which parts of a reading passage are real and which parts are make-believe, you are **distinguishing between real and make-believe.**

★ Real stories are about events that could really happen.

★ Make-believe stories are about events that could not really happen. Clues that signal a story is make-believe are unlikely or magical events, imaginary places, talking animals, and characters who do impossible things.

★ Often, some parts of a story are real, and other parts are make-believe.

Read this story about a girl named Angela. As you read, think about which things in the story could really happen and which things could not really happen. Then answer the questions.

Angela never has to be woken up on Saturdays. On Saturday mornings, Angela jumps out of bed. Saturday is ballet day. Angela can't wait to get to class.

Right after breakfast, Angela gets ready to go to the ballet studio. She pulls her hair back into a bun. She stuffs her ballet shoes into her bag.

As her mother drives her to class, Angela begins to daydream. She sees herself on the center of a stage. She is wearing a glittering costume. On her feet are her magic dance shoes. Angela's feet begin to move as her magic shoes take over. She performs her routine beautifully. The audience cheers as Angela takes a bow.

1. Which of these could not really happen?
   Ⓐ Angela jumps out of bed.
   Ⓑ Angela gets ready for ballet class.
   Ⓒ Angela wears a glittering costume.
   Ⓓ Angela puts on her magic dance shoes.

2. How do you know that this story is mostly real?
   Ⓐ Many dancers have magic ballet shoes.
   Ⓑ People can really take ballet lessons.
   Ⓒ Daydreams tell about things that are real.
   Ⓓ No one can dance without a pair of magic shoes.

 Work with a partner. Talk about your answers to questions 1 and 2. Tell why you chose the answers you did.

Remember: Some things you read are real, and some things are make-believe.

★ To figure out if what you are reading is mostly real, ask yourself, "Could all of the events really happen? Do the characters act as they might in real life?"

★ To figure out if what you are reading is mostly make-believe, ask yourself, "Are any of the events unlikely or magical? Do animals talk? Do characters do impossible things?"

Read this story about a boy who finds some new pets. As you read, ask yourself, "Which parts of the story are mostly real?" Then answer the questions.

Eddie's New Pets

Eddie went exploring in his backyard. He was searching for crickets. When he found two of them, he scooped them up and put them into a jar. He added some dirt, some leaves, and a small stick. He then put the lid on the jar and poked two holes in the top. Eddie then placed his new pets on a windowsill in his bedroom.

That night, as Eddie crawled into bed, he said goodnight to his crickets. "Good night," replied one of the crickets. Eddie blinked his eyes and looked closer into the jar. He saw a cricket knocking on the glass. "Will you set us free tomorrow?" asked the cricket. "Our parents are going to be worried about us."

3. Which of these could really happen?
   Ⓐ Eddie's crickets ask to be freed.
   Ⓑ Eddie puts two crickets into a jar.
   Ⓒ Eddie sees a cricket knock on the side of the jar.
   Ⓓ Eddie's cricket says "good night."

4. How do you know that this story is mostly make-believe?
   Ⓐ Boys can't go exploring in their backyard.
   Ⓑ No one places jars on a windowsill.
   Ⓒ People do not say "good night" to their pets.
   Ⓓ Pets cannot talk to their owners.

Look at the answer choices for each question. Read why each answer choice is correct or not correct.

3. Which of these could really happen?

   Ⓐ Eddie's crickets ask to be freed.

   This answer is not correct because crickets cannot talk. This part of the story is make-believe. It could not really happen.

   ● Eddie puts two crickets into a jar.

   This answer is correct because a boy could really put two crickets into a jar. This part of the story is real. It could really happen.

   Ⓒ Eddie sees a cricket knock on the side of the jar.

   This answer is not correct because crickets cannot knock. This part of the story is make-believe. It could not really happen.

   Ⓓ Eddie's cricket says "good night."

   This answer is not correct because crickets cannot talk. This part of the story is make-believe. It could not really happen.

4. How do you know that this story is mostly make-believe?

   Ⓐ Boys can't go exploring in their backyard.

   This answer is not correct because boys could really go exploring in their backyard.

   Ⓑ No one places jars on a windowsill.

   This answer is not correct because people could really place jars on a windowsill.

   Ⓒ People do not say "good night" to their pets.

   This answer is not correct because people could really say good night to their pets.

   ● Pets cannot talk to their owners.

   This answer is correct because pets cannot talk to their owners.

★ Real stories include biographies, news reports, and informational articles.
★ Make-believe stories include fables, fairy tales, folktales, myths, legends, tall tales, and science fiction.

Read this letter written by one friend to another. Then answer the questions.

July 20, 2000

Dear Sarah,

How is your new house? Many things have changed in the neighborhood since you moved away.

My cat, Fluffy, hasn't been acting like himself lately. I think he misses you. I wish he could talk and tell me what's wrong.

The family that moved into your house seems strange. They don't come out of the house very often, and when they do, they never say hello. Their curtains are drawn all day. My brother says that maybe they're from outer space.

Last week, I couldn't even go to swim class because I was as sick as a dog! I am in level four now. I hope I reach level five before the end of the summer.

When can you come and visit? Write soon, and let me know.

Love,
Noriko

5. Which of these could really happen?
   Ⓐ Sarah comes to visit Noriko.
   Ⓑ The new neighbors come from Mars.
   Ⓒ Noriko blinks her eyes, and Sarah appears.
   Ⓓ Noriko's cat tells her what's wrong.

6. You can tell that the information in the letter is mostly real because
   Ⓐ no one has new neighbors.
   Ⓑ Noriko has a cat that talks.
   Ⓒ the letter tells about things that could really happen.
   Ⓓ people often act like dogs when they are sick.

7. Which of these could not really happen?
   Ⓐ Noriko receives a letter from Sarah.
   Ⓑ Noriko becomes friends with the new neighbors.
   Ⓒ Noriko is sick and turns into a dog.
   Ⓓ Noriko reaches level five in her swim class.

8. Which of these could really happen?
   Ⓐ A new family moves into Sarah's old house.
   Ⓑ A new neighbor travels to outer space.
   Ⓒ Noriko's cat tells Sarah that he misses her.
   Ⓓ Sarah's swim teacher is a fairy princess.

Read this poem about a well-known stuffed bear. Then answer the questions.

Us Two
by A. A. Milne

Wherever I am, there's always Pooh,
There's always Pooh and Me.
Whatever I do, he wants to do,
"Where are you going today?" says Pooh:
"Well, that's very odd 'cos I was too.
Let's go together," says Pooh, says he.
Let's go together," says Pooh.

"What's twice eleven?" I said to Pooh.
("Twice what?" said Pooh to Me.)
"I *think* it ought to be twenty-two."
"Just what I think myself," said Pooh.
"It wasn't an easy sum to do,
But that's what it is," said Pooh, said he.
"That's what it is," said Pooh.

"Let's look for dragons," I said to Pooh.
"Yes, let's," said Pooh to Me.
We crossed the river and found a few—
"Yes, those are dragons all right," said Pooh.
"As soon as I saw their beaks I knew.
That's what they are," said Pooh, said he.
"That's what they are," said Pooh.

"Let's frighten the dragons," I said to Pooh.
"That's right," said Pooh to Me.
"*I'm* not afraid," I said to Pooh,
And I held his paw and I shouted "Shoo!
Silly old dragons!"—and off they flew.
"I wasn't afraid," said Pooh, said he,
"I'm *never* afraid with you."

So wherever I am, there's always Pooh,
There's always Pooh and Me.
"What would I do?" I said to Pooh,
"If it wasn't for you," and Pooh said: "True,
It isn't much fun for One, but Two
Can stick together," says Pooh, says he.
"That's how it is," says Pooh.

9. Which of these could really happen?
   Ⓐ A boy plays with a stuffed bear.
   Ⓑ A stuffed bear talks.
   Ⓒ A boy finds a dragon.
   Ⓓ A stuffed bear is afraid.

10. Which of these could not really happen?
    Ⓐ A boy holds a stuffed bear's hand.
    Ⓑ A boy solves math problems.
    Ⓒ A boy frightens dragons.
    Ⓓ A boy reads a story about dragons.

11. Which of these could really happen?
    Ⓐ Two friends cross a river.
    Ⓑ A dragon becomes frightened.
    Ⓒ A stuffed bear feels safe with a friend.
    Ⓓ A boy listens to his stuffed bear.

12. Which of these could not really happen?
    Ⓐ A boy decides how to spend his day.
    Ⓑ A boy and a stuffed bear talk about their adventure.
    Ⓒ A boy hugs his stuffed bear.
    Ⓓ A boy wonders if dragons are real.

★ A test question about distinguishing between real and make-believe may ask you to tell the difference between things that could happen in real life and things that could not.

★ A test question about distinguishing between real and make-believe often contains the words *could really happen* or *could not really happen*.

Here is a fable written by Aesop. Read the fable. Then do Numbers 13 and 14.

> **The Caged Bird and the Bat**
>
> A singing bird was confined in a cage, which hung outside a window. The bird had a way of singing at night when all other birds were asleep. One night, a bat came and clung to the bars of the cage. The bat asked the bird why she was silent all day and sang only at night.
>
> "I have a very good reason for doing so," said the bird. "It was once when I was singing in the daytime that a man was attracted by my voice. So he set his nets for me and caught me. Since then, I have never sung except by night."
>
> But the bat replied, "It is no use your doing that now when you are a prisoner. If only you had done so before you were caught, you might still be free."

Distinguishing Between Real and Make-believe

13. Which of these could really happen?
    - Ⓐ A man catches a bird.
    - Ⓑ A man turns into a bird.
    - Ⓒ A bird writes a song.
    - Ⓓ A bird teaches a bat to sing.

Distinguishing Between Real and Make-believe

14. Which of these could not really happen?
    - Ⓐ A bird lives in a cage.
    - Ⓑ A bat talks to a bird.
    - Ⓒ A bird stays silent all day.
    - Ⓓ A bat flies near a birdcage.

Here is a fairy tale. Read the fairy tale. Then do Numbers 15 and 16.

The Frog Prince

Of all the toys the princess had, she loved her golden ball the most. One day, the ball bounced in a deep, dark well. The princess began to cry when she heard a deep voice say, "If I get your ball back, will you promise me something?" The princess looked up to see a frog. The princess said she would promise him anything if he got her ball back.

So the frog dove down and quickly came back up with the ball. "What do you want me to promise?" asked the happy princess.

"That you will let me live with you and be your friend," answered the frog.

"I'll have to think about that," said the princess. The frog could see that the princess didn't want to be his friend. So, tearfully, he said good-bye.

"Wait," said the princess. "Don't be sad. I'll be your friend." She picked him up and kissed him.

Suddenly, the frog was gone, and in his place stood a fine prince, who said, "Only the kiss of a kind-hearted princess could remove the spell that a witch put on me." The prince and the princess became good friends. One day, they decided to marry. And they lived happily ever after.

Distinguishing Between Real and Make-believe

15. Which of these could not really happen?
   Ⓐ A ball bounces into a well.
   Ⓑ A frog dives into well.
   Ⓒ A frog says a tearful good-bye.
   Ⓓ A princess becomes friends with a prince.

Distinguishing Between Real and Make-believe

16. Which of these could really happen?
   Ⓐ A frog talks to a princess.
   Ⓑ A frog does a favor for a princess.
   Ⓒ A witch turns a prince into a frog.
   Ⓓ A princess cries when she loses her toy.

PART ONE: READ A NOTICE

Here is a notice about a contest. Read the notice.
Then do Numbers 1 through 6.

ATTENTION! ATTENTION! YOUNG ARTISTS!

Do you like to draw or paint? Do you like animals? Would you like to do something to help animals? Then hop like a bunny and pick up a paintbrush. We need you to enter the Abram Wildlife Association's Calendar Contest.

Every year, the Abram Wildlife Association creates a calendar. We want next year's calendar to show your artwork. We will choose 15 winners from the drawings and paintings we receive. The winning artwork will appear in next year's calendar, "Young Artists Look at Animals." Send us your artwork, based on one of these themes.

- People Helping Animals
- Animal Babies
- Endangered Animals
- Troubled Habitats
- Wild Animals Are Not Pets

Your art could be the first step in saving the life of an endangered animal. Don't say you're too busy. Make time to help save the world's wild animals!

For more information about helping animals, call 1-800-555-HELP.

Identifying Author's Purpose

1. The author's purpose in paragraph two is to
   Ⓐ explain what the contest is about.
   Ⓑ entertain readers with a story about animals.
   Ⓒ persuade readers to help animals.
   Ⓓ describe the work of the Abram Wildlife Association.

Identifying Author's Purpose

2. What is the author's purpose in the last paragraph?
   Ⓐ to inform readers how to enter the contest
   Ⓑ to persuade readers to enter the contest
   Ⓒ to describe a prize-winning poster
   Ⓓ to entertain readers with silly animal stories

Interpreting Figurative Language

3. In the last paragraph, what is the meaning of the phrase *make time*?
   Ⓐ "look at one's watch"
   Ⓑ "draw a clock"
   Ⓒ "wait to do something"
   Ⓓ "do something even if one is busy"

Interpreting Figurative Language

4. Which of these is a simile?
   Ⓐ hop like a bunny
   Ⓑ you like to draw
   Ⓒ you like animals
   Ⓓ like to do something

Distinguishing Between Real and Make-believe

5. Which of these could really happen?
   Ⓐ A boy from the planet Venus wins the contest.
   Ⓑ A dog draws a poster and sends it to the contest.
   Ⓒ Every year, the Abram Wildlife Association creates a calendar.
   Ⓓ One of the contest judges is a lion.

Distinguishing Between Real and Make-believe

6. Which of these could not really happen?
   Ⓐ A tiger lives happily in an apartment.
   Ⓑ Children help save wild animals.
   Ⓒ Some wild animals are in danger.
   Ⓓ Wild animals live in the United States.

Here is an article about wild animals. Read the article.
Then do Numbers 7 through 12.

Animal House

Where the Wild Things Live!

The Wildlife Rescue Center in Vista, California, has a full house. Injured animals call it home all year long. But when spring arrives, the Center gets tons of calls about orphaned baby animals.

"We get the babies after something has happened to their parents," Bob Farner says. He runs the Rescue Center. Because so many baby animals need care, Bob takes them to other wildlife centers in the area.

Most of the orphaned babies are raised in people's houses. These volunteers are like parents to the animals. One year, Bob had more than 400 orphaned baby swallows. "A volunteer took care of them at home!" he says. "When the swallows learned to fly, we released them where other swallows lived."

Injured animals that don't get better stay at the Center. Hawks, crows, bobcats, raccoons, and a mountain lion live at the Center. "They help teach people about animals and the environment," Bob says.

Last year, the Center returned more than 2,000 baby animals to nature. Now that's really wild!

Identifying Author's Purpose

7. The author wrote the article mainly to
   - (A) entertain readers with a funny animal story.
   - (B) explain what happens at the Wildlife Rescue Center.
   - (C) persuade readers to bring animals to the Wildlife Rescue Center.
   - (D) describe the animals at the Wildlife Rescue Center.

Identifying Author's Purpose

8. You know your answer to question 7 is correct because the article mainly
   - (A) describes the animals that are rescued.
   - (B) provides facts about a person, place, or thing.
   - (C) tries to convince readers to do something.
   - (D) tells an enjoyable story.

Interpreting Figurative Language

9. In the first paragraph, the phrase *call it home* means
   - (A) "speak."
   - (B) "dwell."
   - (C) "attend."
   - (D) "move in."

Interpreting Figurative Language

10. In paragraph three, the volunteers are compared to
    - (A) babies.
    - (B) swallows.
    - (C) parents.
    - (D) orphans.

Distinguishing Between Real and Make-believe

11. Which of these could really happen at the Wildlife Rescue Center?
    - (A) A volunteer takes care of 200 baby swallows.
    - (B) A volunteer teaches a crow to ride a bicycle.
    - (C) Animals at the Center talk to people about the environment.
    - (D) A bobcat learns how to fly.

Distinguishing Between Real and Make-believe

12. Which of these could not really happen?
    - (A) Orphaned animals are raised in people's houses.
    - (B) Baby animals lose their parents.
    - (C) Healthy animals volunteer to take care of injured animals.
    - (D) Injured animals that get better are returned to nature.

PART ONE: READ A FOLKTALE

Here is a Native-American folktale. Read the folktale.
Then do Numbers 1 through 12.

The First Medicine

Once upon a time, a very sick old man entered an Iroquois village. Over each wigwam, there was a sign. The sign told to which clan the owner of the wigwam belonged. A beaver skin meant that the owner was of the beaver clan. A deer skin meant that the owner was of the deer clan. The old man went to each wigwam asking for food and a place to sleep. But each time, he was sent away.

Finally, he came to a wigwam with a bear skin. A kind woman lived there. She let the man into her wigwam. The old man told the woman to go out and search for certain herbs. She prepared these herbs, following the old man's directions. The old man took the medicine and became better in no time.

A few days later, the old man came down with a fever. This time, he told the woman to search for different herbs. Again, this medicine healed him. This was repeated many times. Each time the old man became sick, the woman would gather different herbs, make a new medicine, and cure him.

At last, the old man told the woman that she now knew all the secrets for curing diseases. He told her to plant a hemlock tree in front of her wigwam. The tree would grow high in the air above all others. This would show that the bear clan ranks higher than all other clans.

Finding Main Idea

1. The folktale is mostly about
   - Ⓐ how a woman learned the secrets of medicine.
   - Ⓑ what the signs over Iroquois wigwams meant.
   - Ⓒ why there are so many hemlock trees.
   - Ⓓ how medicine is made from plants.

Recognizing Cause and Effect

4. What happened each time the old man became sick?
   - Ⓐ The woman went out to search for bears.
   - Ⓑ The people of the village turned him away.
   - Ⓒ He showed the woman how to make a new medicine.
   - Ⓓ The woman planted a hemlock tree in front of her wigwam.

Recalling Facts and Details

2. In the folktale, which of these animal skins was not found in the Iroquois village?
   - Ⓐ beaver
   - Ⓑ bear
   - Ⓒ coyote
   - Ⓓ deer

Comparing and Contrasting

5. How was the woman of the bear clan different from the other people in the village?
   - Ⓐ She did not turn the old man away.
   - Ⓑ She had more room in her wigwam.
   - Ⓒ She had an animal skin over her wigwam.
   - Ⓓ She knew the old man had the secret of medicine.

Understanding Sequence

3. Which of these happened last?
   - Ⓐ The old man went to each wigwam looking for food and a place to sleep.
   - Ⓑ A kind woman let the old man in.
   - Ⓒ The old man entered an Iroquois village.
   - Ⓓ The old man came down with a fever.

Making Predictions

6. The next time a sick old man enters the Iroquois village, the people will probably
   - Ⓐ run away from the village and hide.
   - Ⓑ order the woman to cure him.
   - Ⓒ send him away, as they did before.
   - Ⓓ try to help him as much as possible.

Finding Word Meaning in Context

7. The word *ranks* in the last paragraph means
   - Ⓐ "sings or makes a noise."
   - Ⓑ "has a position in a group."
   - Ⓒ "gives off a strong smell."
   - Ⓓ "lives in a certain place."

Identifying Author's Purpose

10. The author probably wrote the folktale to
    - Ⓐ describe what an Iroquois village looked like.
    - Ⓑ get readers to learn more about the Iroquois.
    - Ⓒ explain why the bear clan has a high place among the Iroquois.
    - Ⓓ entertain readers with a story that tells about the first medicines.

Drawing Conclusions and Making Inferences

8. From the folktale, you can tell that
   - Ⓐ the old man did not want to share his secrets with the woman.
   - Ⓑ wigwams were made from a variety of animal skins.
   - Ⓒ the old man shared his secrets with the woman because she was willing to help him.
   - Ⓓ all diseases can be cured with herbs.

Interpreting Figurative Language

11. In the folktale, the phrase *in no time* means
    - Ⓐ "quickly."
    - Ⓑ "never."
    - Ⓒ "slowly."
    - Ⓓ "quietly."

Distinguishing Between Fact and Opinion

9. Which of these is a fact?
   - Ⓐ The deer clan is better than the bear clan.
   - Ⓑ The old man is very smart.
   - Ⓒ Most people in the village were selfish.
   - Ⓓ The woman followed the old man's directions.

Distinguishing Between Real and Make-believe

12. Which of these could not really happen?
    - Ⓐ A sick old man enters an Iroquois village.
    - Ⓑ A bear gathers herbs to make medicine.
    - Ⓒ A kind woman lets an old man into her wigwam.
    - Ⓓ A hemlock tree grows to be very tall.

Here is an article about how Jewish people arrived in America. Read the article. Then do Numbers 13 through 24.

We all know that Christopher Columbus sailed across the Atlantic in 1492. The story of his trip has been retold many times.

Do you remember King Ferdinand and Queen Isabella from the story of Columbus? They were the king and queen of Spain. They gave Columbus the money he needed to make his trip. The king and queen were not always so generous, though.

In the same year that Columbus set sail, the king and queen passed a new law. They made up their mind that they did not want Jewish people living in their country. The new law forced all Jews to leave Spain at once.

Some Jewish families went to live in Portugal. Later, some of these families settled in South America. As years passed, however, Jews living in South America were also told to leave.

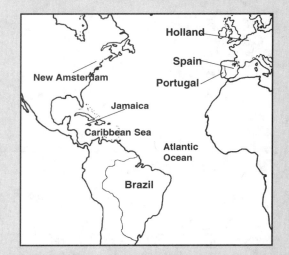

In 1645, a group of Jews living in Brazil decided to go to Holland. As their ship sailed through the Caribbean Sea, a storm caused them to stop in Jamaica. While they waited there, they ran out of money. They were not able to pay for the long trip to Holland. Instead, they set sail on a ship headed to New Amsterdam, a Dutch colony.

One day in September 1645, their ship landed in New Amsterdam. Today we know New Amsterdam as New York City. That day, 23 Jewish passengers stepped off the boat and into history. The history of Jewish people in the United States began with their arrival.

Finding Main Idea

13. The best title for the article is
    Ⓐ "1492: An Important Year."
    Ⓑ "The Dutch Colony of New Amsterdam."
    Ⓒ "The Journey of Christopher Columbus."
    Ⓓ "How Jewish People Came to the United States."

Recalling Facts and Details

14. When a storm forced them to stop in Jamaica, the Jews had been sailing to
    Ⓐ Spain.
    Ⓑ Portugal.
    Ⓒ Brazil.
    Ⓓ Holland.

Understanding Sequence

15. These boxes tell some things that happened in the article.

The king and queen force all Jews out of Spain.	Jews in South America are forced to leave.	
1	2	3

What belongs in box 3?
    Ⓐ Jewish passengers arrive in New Amsterdam.
    Ⓑ The king and queen pass a new law.
    Ⓒ Some Jews leave Portugal for Brazil.
    Ⓓ Columbus sailed across the Atlantic.

Recognizing Cause and Effect

16. The Jews did not go to Holland because
    Ⓐ they weren't allowed there.
    Ⓑ there was a storm in the Caribbean Sea.
    Ⓒ the king and queen would not let them.
    Ⓓ they thought New Amsterdam would be a better place to live.

Comparing and Contrasting

17. According to the article, how were Brazil and Spain alike?
    Ⓐ Both countries have the same laws.
    Ⓑ The people of both countries spoke the same language.
    Ⓒ Both countries forced Jewish people to leave.
    Ⓓ Both countries are ruled by kings and queens.

Making Predictions

18. What probably happened to the Jewish people who came to New Amsterdam?
    Ⓐ They soon left to return to Brazil.
    Ⓑ A new law was passed that forced them to leave.
    Ⓒ They stayed and were later joined by other Jewish families.
    Ⓓ They returned to Spain after the king and queen no longer ruled.

Finding Word Meaning in Context

19. In paragraph two, the word *generous* means
    - Ⓐ "fond of all people."
    - Ⓑ "happy to help others."
    - Ⓒ "unkind to others."
    - Ⓓ "fair in all things."

Identifying Author's Purpose

22. The author's purpose in paragraph two is to
    - Ⓐ describe the country of Spain.
    - Ⓑ get readers to feel sorry for the Spanish Jews.
    - Ⓒ entertain readers with a tale about Columbus.
    - Ⓓ explain something about the king and queen of Spain.

Drawing Conclusions and Making Inferences

20. From the article, you can tell that
    - Ⓐ the king and queen passed a new law in 1492.
    - Ⓑ the people of Brazil welcomed the Jews.
    - Ⓒ life in Portugal was difficult for the Jews.
    - Ⓓ most people did not obey the new law passed by the king and queen of Spain.

Interpreting Figurative Language

23. In paragraph three, the phrase *made up their mind* means
    - Ⓐ "passed a law."
    - Ⓑ "acted unfairly."
    - Ⓒ "made a mistake."
    - Ⓓ "made a decision."

Distinguishing Between Fact and Opinion

21. Which of these is an opinion?
    - Ⓐ Columbus sailed across the Atlantic in 1492.
    - Ⓑ Twenty-three Jews arrived in New Amsterdam in 1645.
    - Ⓒ What happened to the Jews in Spain was terrible.
    - Ⓓ After the Jews were forced out of Spain, they settled in different places.

Distinguishing Between Real and Make-believe

24. Which of these could not really happen?
    - Ⓐ Jewish people were forced to leave their homes.
    - Ⓑ The king and queen of Spain didn't want Jewish people living in Spain.
    - Ⓒ There was a big storm in the Caribbean Sea.
    - Ⓓ The Jewish families watched television on their way to New Amsterdam.

Here is a story about some birds you may have seen. Read the story. Then do Numbers 25 through 36.

Springtime! Canada geese are returning to their homes in the north. But they must hurry. It's almost time to lay their eggs.

A pair of geese leaves the flock and lands beside a shimmering lake. They are tired, but they can't rest yet. They must find a place to build a nest.

They see a quiet spot hidden among tall reeds and marsh grasses. Here, the nest will be safe from enemies.

The mother goose builds her nest with leaves and dried grass. She lines it with soft feathers plucked from her own breast. When the nest is finished, she climbs in and lays four tan eggs.

The mother sits on her eggs, while the father goose swims close by in case of trouble. Almost thirty days must pass before the eggs will hatch into baby goslings. But the mother goose still needs to eat and bathe. She covers the eggs with feathers and grass to hide them and keep them warm until she returns.

But look! Something's moving in the tall grass, and it's headed this way. A hungry raccoon creeps closer and closer. The raccoon stops, arches its tail over its back, and sniffs the air. It's about to steal an egg for breakfast.

The raccoon reaches toward the eggs with sharp-clawed paws. Suddenly, an angry hiss shatters the quiet. Powerful wings flap wildly as the father goose roars toward the surprised bandit.

"HONK! HONK! HONK!" warns the angry goose. "Leave those eggs alone!"

The frightened raccoon runs away into the woods. There'll be no eggs for breakfast today!

Days later, mother and father goose are rewarded for their care. Four tan eggs finally hatch.

Hello, baby goslings!

Finding Main Idea

25. Which of these is the best title for the story?
  Ⓐ "Water Birds"
  Ⓑ "Goose on Guard"
  Ⓒ "Birds I Have Known"
  Ⓓ "How Geese Build Nests"

Recalling Facts and Details

26. What does the mother goose use to build a nest?
  Ⓐ leaves, dried grass, and feathers
  Ⓑ sticks, rocks, and mud
  Ⓒ hair, grass, and shells
  Ⓓ rocks, scissors, and paper

Understanding Sequence

27. The boxes tell some things that happened in the story.

	The mother goose builds a nest and climbs in.	The mother goose sits on the eggs while the father swims close by.
1	2	3

What belongs in box 1?
  Ⓐ The mother goose lays four eggs.
  Ⓑ A hungry raccoon creeps closer to the eggs.
  Ⓒ The mother and father geese return to their home in the north.
  Ⓓ Four tan eggs finally hatch.

Recognizing Cause and Effect

28. Why did the raccoon run into the woods?
  Ⓐ It was no longer hungry.
  Ⓑ The father goose scared it away.
  Ⓒ It was frightened by the four baby geese.
  Ⓓ It wanted to hide before it was seen by the father goose.

Comparing and Contrasting

29. What is one way that the mother goose and the father goose are different?
  Ⓐ The father flies south in the spring, but the mother does not.
  Ⓑ The mother is rewarded for her care, but the father is not.
  Ⓒ The father can fly, but the mother cannot.
  Ⓓ The mother sits on the eggs, but the father protects the eggs.

Making Predictions

30. What will probably happen now that the baby geese are born?
  Ⓐ The father will take care of them.
  Ⓑ They will fly south with their parents.
  Ⓒ The mother and father will fly away and leave them alone.
  Ⓓ The mother will take care of them until they can take care of themselves.

Finding Word Meaning in Context

31. From the story, you can tell that a *gosling* is
- Ⓐ a mother goose.
- Ⓑ a baby goose.
- Ⓒ a father goose.
- Ⓓ an angry goose.

Identifying Author's Purpose

34. The author probably wrote the story to
- Ⓐ describe how to build a nest for a goose.
- Ⓑ explain why geese fly north in the spring.
- Ⓒ get readers to read more books about geese.
- Ⓓ entertain readers with an enjoyable story about geese.

Drawing Conclusions and Making Inferences

32. You can tell from the story that geese
- Ⓐ are friendly with raccoons.
- Ⓑ take good care of their babies.
- Ⓒ learn to swim right after they are born.
- Ⓓ fly south to lay their eggs.

Interpreting Figurative Language

35. In the story, the phrase *headed this way* means
- Ⓐ "coming in this direction."
- Ⓑ "hiding in the woods."
- Ⓒ "sneaking through the grass."
- Ⓓ "looking for a meal."

Distinguishing Between Fact and Opinion

33. Which of these is not a fact?
- Ⓐ Geese build nests in safe places.
- Ⓑ Raccoons are nasty animals.
- Ⓒ Raccoons have sharp claws on their paws.
- Ⓓ Almost 30 days must pass before goose eggs hatch.

Distinguishing Between Real and Make-believe

36. Which of these could really happen?
- Ⓐ Geese and raccoons live together happily.
- Ⓑ A father goose yells at a raccoon.
- Ⓒ A mother goose leaves her nest.
- Ⓓ A father goose lays four eggs.

ACKNOWLEDGMENTS

Curriculum Associates wishes to thank the following authors and publishers
for their permission to reprint copyrighted material. Every effort has been made
to locate all copyright holders. Any errors or omissions in copyright notice
are inadvertent and will be credited in future printings as they are discovered.

page 30: "Whistle, Johanna" by Siv Cedering. Reprinted by permission of the author who retains the copyright. © 1997 by Siv Cedering.

page 58: "The Painter and the Judge" from *SOUTH AND NORTH, EAST AND WEST* Edited text © 1992 Michael Rosen. Reproduced by permission of Walker Books ltd., London. Published in the US by Candlewick Press Inc., Cambridge, MA.

page 61: "Butterfly Song," from *In the Trail of the Wind*, edited by John Bierhorst, from *Bureau of American Ethnology*, Bulletin 165, 1957, page 38.

page 69: "Shirt Button" by Diane Mayr. Reprinted by permission of LADYBUG magazine, February 1998, Vol. 8, No. 6, © 1998 by Diane Mayr.

page 72: "Global Food" from KID CITY, November 1997. Copyright 1997 Children's Television Workshop (New York, New York). All rights reserved.

page 94: "Drinking Straw Curtain," used with permission of Sterling Publishing Co., Inc., 387 Park Avenue South, New York, NY 10016 from *CUPS & CANS & PAPER PLATE FANS: Craft Projects from Recycled Materials* © 1992 by Phyllis & Noel Fiarotta.

page 109: "Us Two" by A. A. Milne, from *Now We Are Six*, by A. A. Milne, illustrations by E. H. Shepard. Copyright 1927 by E.P. Dutton, renewed © 1955 by A. A. Milne. Used by permission of Dutton Children's Books, a division of Penguin Putnam Inc.

page 114: "Animal House: Where the Wild Things Live!" from KID CITY, May 1998. Copyright 1998 Children's Television Workshop (New York, New York). All rights reserved.

page 122: "Goose on Guard" by Eileen Ross. Reprinted by permission of LADYBUG magazine, May 1998, Vol. 8, No. 9, © 1998 by Eileen Ross.

Illustration Credits

Susan Hawk/pages 39, 40, 42, 53, 58, 62, 65, 68, 70, 81, 86, 105, 106, 111, and 116

Jamie Ruh/pages 4, 8, 10, 14, 17, 19, 20, 22, 25, 30, 32, 34, 48, 55, and 60

Photography Credits

Jamie Ruh/pages 37 and 56

www.arttoday.com/pages 12, 19, 76, 98, and 114

Library of Congress, By Popular Demand: Jackie Robinson and Other Baseball Highlights, 1860s–1960s, LC-USZ62-119882/page 27

Courtesy of Children's Defense Fund, Washington, D.C./page 84

Courtesy of Federation Internationale de Football Association, Zurich, Switzerland/page 101

Courtesy of HarperCollins/page 50

Developer and Writer: Maureen Sotoohi

Editor: Deborah Adcock

Designer: Jamie Ruh